Indian Statistical Series No. 18

THE APPROACH OF OPERATIONAL RESEARCH TO PLANNING IN INDIA

INDIAN STATISTICAL INSTITUTE

THE APPROACH OF OPERATIONAL RESEARCH TO PLANNING IN INDIA

P. C. MAHALANOBIS

ASIA PUBLISHING HOUSE
New York

STATISTICAL PUBLISHING SOCIETY
Calcutta

Indian Statistical Series No. 18

THE APPROACH OF OPERATIONAL RESEARCH TO PLANNING IN INDIA

© INDIAN STATISTICAL INSTITUTE
1963

PRINTED IN INDIA

by Kalipada Mukherjee at Eka Press, 204/1 Barrackpore Trunk Road, Calcutta-35
and published jointly by P. S. Jayasinghe, Asia Publishing House, Bombay and
Statistical Publishing Society, Calcutta

PREFACE

This paper was originally written to explain the logical and factual basis of the recommendations for the formulation of the Second Five Year Plan which was submitted to Shri Jawaharlal Nehru, Prime Minister of India, on 17 March 1955. The paper was published in *Sankhyā* : The Indian Journal of Statistics, Vol. 16, 1955. The paper is now published in a book form with some editing changes to make it more easily available to persons interested in economic planning in India.

29 June 1963   *P. C. Mahalanobis*

CONTENTS

THE APPROACH OF OPERATIONAL RESEARCH TO PLANNING IN INDIA

CHAPTER 1

RECENT DEVELOPMENTS IN PLANNING

1. The Draft Plan-frame of 17 March 1955 giving Recommendations for the Formulation of the Second Five Year Plan of India (to be referred to subsequently as the Plan-frame) together with extracts from the associated working paper of 21 March 1955 prepared jointly by the Economic Division of the Ministry of Finance, and the Economic Division of the Planning Commission in consultation with the Central Statistical Organization and the Indian Statistical Institute, and a memorandum giving "Basic Considerations Relating to the Plan-frame" prepared on 10 April 1955 by the Panel of Economists of the Planning Commission are being reproduced as appendices by the courtesy of the Planning Commission.

2. The Plan-frame was addressed to plan-making organisations of the country, and contains only such information as was likely to be useful for preparing plan projects. For readers who are not in direct touch with planning in India the mode of presentation of the Plan-frame is not adequate. Any approach to planning which involves social action has to be judged in its historical context. I shall therefore try to explain briefly my own approach to the problem; the circumstances in which the Plan-frame was drafted; and its logical and statistical basis. I shall discuss in a separate paper what would be the implications of the present approach on the future course of planning in India. I have used a personal form of narration because the views expressed in this paper are my own and are not necessarily shared by other persons or agencies with which I am connected.

STATISTICAL DEVELOPMENTS

3. During the greater part of my working life I have been a teacher of physics; but in the early twenties I started using statistical methods to solve problems mostly of practical importance

but also sometimes of theoretical interest. My statistical work increased considerably since the establishment of the Indian Statistical Institute in 1931-32. At the desire of Prime Minister Jawaharlal Nehru, I started working as the Honorary Statistical Adviser to the Cabinet, Government of India, from February 1949. In the same year I agreed somewhat reluctantly to become the Chairman of the National Income Committee with Professor D. R. Gadgil and Dr. V. K. R. V. Rao as members. My colleagues did a great service in laying sound foundations for national income statistics and making a thorough review of the gaps in statistical information in India. In this country many of these gaps can be filled only through the method of sampling, and it was a significant advance when the Government of India decided to initiate the National Sample Survey (NSS) which is operating continually since 1950 in the form of about two complete "rounds" per year covering both rural and urban areas of the whole country. The field staff works under the direct control of the Ministry of Finance ; and the statistical work (sample design, processing and analysis of data) is done in the Indian Statistical Institute. The NSS can supply much information required for planning.

4. A Central Statistical Unit had been started in February 1949 and was converted into the Central Statistical Organization (CSO) two years later. It is now a pivotal agency for general coordination and the development of comparable concepts, definitions, and standards on a country-wide basis. The CSO works in close touch with the statistical offices in the Central Ministries as well as with the Statistical Bureaus in the various States of India. Rapid developments have also taken place in the Indian Statistical Institute (ISI), a non-profit scientific institution, which works in close association with Government. The CSO, the NSS, and the Institute provide a good statistical base for technical work relating to planning.

THE PLANNING COMMISSION

5. The Prime Minister had been keenly interested in planning for a very long time. It was because of this personal interest that he was appointed Chairman of the National Planning Committee which was set up by the Indian National Congress Party in 1938. This Planning Committee published a number of valuable reports most of which, however, became out of date after the war. The Planning Commission, with the Prime Minister as Chairman, was

established in 1950. It prepared the First Five Year Plan of India for the period 1951-52 to 1955-56 ; and is now actively engaged in preparing the Second Five Year Plan.

6. As Statistical Adviser I have been connected with the Planning Commission from the beginning. My contact with Government made me increasingly aware of the poverty of the great masses of people, and the inadequacy of the techniques of production. It has been always my view that statistics is an applied science and its chief object is to help in solving practical problems. Poverty is the most basic problem of the country; and statistics must help in solving this problem.

Some Earlier Work

7. I expressed my views of this period in my presidential address entitled "Why Statistics ?" to the Indian Science Congress held in Poona in 1950. In this paper I used a ratio of the value of product to the capital invested to make preliminary calculations about industrial development; this ratio was subsequently found useful in studies on planning. When the First Five Year Plan was being finalised in 1951 I stressed that a progressive and integrated economic policy, rather than a reliance on a number of useful but unconnected projects or on some parametric marginal rate of saving, would be necessary to achieve a high rate of growth. In 1952, in a lecture delivered at the National Institute of Sciences of India, I put forward certain views on planning; and pointed out that it was necessary to increase the rate of investment from 5 or 6 per cent to 10 or 11 per cent. In a second paper published in *Sankhyā* in 1953, I elaborated these views, and used a model of growth for a planned economy to which reference is made in a later section.

8. Two young colleagues had started working with me from the very beginning. Pitambar Pant, who like me started life as a teacher of physics, has been generally helping me since 1946. He was appointed Private Secretary to the Chairman, Planning Commission, in 1952, and has been actively assisting me in the planning work since then; he is now Deputy Secretary in the Planning Commission. Moni Mukherjee, originally a statistician in the Indian Statistical Institute, who had worked as Secretary, National Income Committee from 1949 to 1953 and is now in charge of the National Income Unit in the CSO, has been closely associated with my work. We went on thinking on our own lines, and I took advantage of my visits abroad to have discussions with

distinguished economists and statisticians. Gradually other workers have joined our group among whom I should like particularly to mention I. G. Patel (of the Economic Division, Ministry of Finance), a young economist, who made significant contributions to our thinking especially on the financial side.

THE APPROACH OF OPERATIONAL RESEARCH TO PLANNING

9. I have been all the time using the approach of operational research with a view to getting some broad idea of the strategy of planning. In December 1953 I told Shri Chintaman D. Deshmukh (Minister of Finance and Member of the Planning Commission in charge of its Economic Division) that a small organized group would be useful. He immediately agreed and sanctioned funds to enable an Operational Research Unit (ORU) being established in the Indian Statistical Institute which made it possible to start some preliminary studies on planning. The ORU also gave us the opportunity to invite distinguished foreign economists and specialists to come to India for short visits to participate in our work. The visit of Professor Charles Bettelheim of Paris (Editor of *Planification*) in the winter season of 1953-54 was particularly stimulating and helpful.

10. I may explain why I have been using the phrase 'operational research' in relation to planning in India. Our aim is to solve the problem of poverty, that is, to find a feasible method of bringing about a continuing economic development of the country. It would be necessary to use much scientific and technical knowledge and also to organize continuing research at various levels for this purpose. But research is not our primary objective; the aim is to solve our particular problem. When a practising physician gives medical treatment to a patient he uses much scientific knowledge and may even do some research, but his chief aim is to cure the patient. His observations or experiments on the patient may add to medical knowledge but the treatment given is not primarily for purposes of research. The distinction is important. In my view our studies also have the primary aim of solving a particular problem (and not of doing any theoretical research for its own sake). This is why I have used the phrase operational research in the present connexion. We are speaking of India and suggesting methods which we think are practicable under Indian conditions. I shall be naturally glad if our work is of help to any other country. But it has not been our intention to formulate

any general theory which would be universally applicable to other countries.

11. I have tried to set up a conceptual frame-work which would be of help for practical purposes; and I have used certain statistical methods to solve our problem. I do not think that the models have any permanent value of their own. I have used them as scaffolding to be dismantled as soon as their purpose has been served. There is, of course, much need of theoretical thinking and researches; but so far we have been primarily concerned with practical issues, that is, with operational (as distinguished from theoretical) research.

FORMULATION OF THE PROBLEM BY THE PLANNING COMMISSION : SEPTEMBER 1954

12. On 14 September 1954 there was a full discussion in the Planning Commission, under the Chairmanship of the Prime Minister, on the basic approach to the formulation of the Second Five Year Plan which was due to begin in 1956-57. At the end of the discussion the Finance Minister asked : "Is it possible to prepare a Plan which would enable unemployment being liquidated in 10 years and which would also provide for a satisfactory increase in national income at the same time?" This was the problem set to us.

13. One important decision was taken by the Planning Commission at the same meeting, namely, that the Central Statistical Organization (CSO) should be responsible for the statistical work of the Planning Commission ; and that the CSO in collaboration with the Indian Statistical Institute (ISI) should immediately take up studies relating to planning. I had another discussion with the Prime Minister on 17 September 1954 about the basic approach to the Second Plan ; and, at his desire, gave him next day a brief note on this subject. He asked me to prepare working papers on the lines of our discussions.

INAUGURATION OF STUDIES ON PLANNING : NOVEMBER 1954

14. Prime Minister Jawaharlal Nehru inaugurated studies relating to planning for national development in the Indian Statistical Institute in Calcutta on 3 November 1954. On 8 November 1954 I submitted to the Prime Minister a general note on planning (which was later circulated as Working Paper No. 1 of the Institute series on planning); and at his desire I explained my views at a meeting

of the National Development Council (which consists of the Central
Cabinet, the Planning Commission and the Chief Ministers of all
the States of India) held in New Delhi on 10 November 1954. From
about this time, the Finance Minister made arrangements by which
Shri J. J. Anjaria (Chief, Economic Division, Planning Commission)
and Shri I. G. Patel (Economic Division of the Ministry of Finance)
became closely associated with our work. A number of study
groups were quickly organized in the Indian Statistical Institute
and a large number of Working Papers were prepared and were
circulated in mimeographed form; some of them are being printed.

15. On 20 and 21 December 1954, the Lok Sabha (the Indian
Parliament) discussed the economic situation in India and at the
end of a long debate adopted a motion that the "objective of our
economic policy should be a socialistic pattern of society and towards this end the tempo of economic activity in general and industrial development in particular should be stepped up to the maximum possible extent." One month later, the Prime Minister raised
the question of the basic approach to planning in India at the
annual session of the Indian National Congress Party at Avadi
where a resolution was passed on 21 January 1955 accepting a
socialistic pattern of society suited to Indian conditions as the
aim of national planning in India. These decisions settled, in
principle, the type of economic development of India in future.

16. The Standing Committee of the National Development
Council which had met on 7 January 1955 and had agreed that
a unified programme should be prepared for the formulation of
the Second Five Year Plan, met again on 27 January and decided
that a Draft Plan-frame containing recommendations for the formulation of the Second Five Year Plan should be got ready by
April 1955. This was followed by several weeks of work at very
high pressure by a small group of economists and statisticians
in the Economic Division of the Ministry of Finance, the Economic
Division of the Planning Commission, the Central Statistical Organization and the Indian Statistical Institute.

17. I should like to mention that in the winter season of 1954-55
a number of distinguished statisticians and economists came to
the Institute from different countries of the world. Among those
who came in connexion with economic planning may be mentioned
Professor Ragnar Frisch of Norway, Professor Oskar Lange of
Poland, Professor Charles Bettelheim of France, Dr. Richard
Goodwin from the University of Cambridge, and Academician

D. D. Degtyar of the Soviet Gosplan at the head of a Soviet team of economists and statisticians (Professor I. Y. Pisarev, Dr. M. I. Rubinstein and Professor P. M. Moskvin) from the USSR Academy of Sciences. We profited much from our discussions with these distinguished experts. They helped us to think clearly ; they made constructive criticisms about the logical basis of our thinking ; and they placed at our disposal their own rich experience ; but, naturally, they refrained from giving any specific advice on questions of policy. The greatest benefit was that through contacts with such eminent experts from many different countries we gained confidence in our way of thinking. The basic decisions naturally had to be taken by the small group of Indian statisticians and economists who were working on the Plan-frame.

18. I should also mention that a Panel of Economists had been set up in January 1955 by the Planning Commission with Shri C. D. Deshmukh as Chairman, Professor D. R. Gadgil as Vice-Chairman and twenty leading economists of India, as members. This Panel met for the first time on 27 and 28 January 1955; and started preparing working papers on a number of subjects relating to planning.

THE DRAFT PLAN-FRAME OF 17 MARCH 1955 AND ASSOCIATED PAPERS

19. I submitted the Draft Plan-frame on 17 March 1955. There was much joint thinking and joint work behind it, and the Draft Plan-frame was truly a cooperative effort although it was issued in my name. The associated working paper giving detailed technical information was submitted on 21 March 1955 and the two papers were sent to the Panel of Economists and were considered by the Panel on 8, 9 and 10 April 1955. The Panel prepared a memorandum on "Basic considerations relating to the Plan-frame" in which they (with the exception of one member) agreed with the basic approach of the Plan-frame and approved generally its proposals and underlying principles. The strong support of the Panel of Economists at this stage was of decisive importance.

20. The Draft Plan-frame, the Joint Working Paper, and the Memorandum by the Panel of Economists were considered on 5 May 1955 by the Standing Committee of the National Development Council and on 6 May by the Council itself which gave general approval to the approach adopted in these papers and desired that the Draft Plan-frame should be used as the basis for discussions

between the Planning Commission and the Central Ministries and State Governments for the formulation of the Second Plan. It was decided to release all the papers for public information. The approach of the Plan-frame and associated papers was subsequently approved at the meeting of the All-India Congress Committee held at Berhampore on 10 May 1955.

21. On the publication of the Draft Plan-frame there was much discussion in the newspapers and at public and group meetings. There was opposition from certain quarters but public opinion appeared to be generally in favour. The subject was again considered by the National Development Council on 24 July 1955 and it was decided that the physical targets of the Plan-frame should be maintained even if this involved an increase in the financial outlay. After further public discussions the Draft Plan-frame and associated papers were examined by the All-India Congress Committee on 3 and 4 September 1955, and the basic approach and targets were again generally approved. The proposals were approved generally for the third time by the National Development Council on 5 September 1955.

22. I should like to point out, at this stage, that I had called the document of 17 March 1955 a "draft of a draft". My intention was that it would be revised and issued as a draft in the form of a document of the Planning Commission. This, however, was not done ; and the Plan-frame was issued in my name in its original form. Its only aim was to supply a convenient starting point for planning within a flexible but connected frame-work.

Chapter 2

PRESENT CONDITIONS IN INDIA

1. India is a vast subcontinent with 12 major language groups[1] and 9 major religious faiths.[2] The country lies between latitudes 8° and 37° north and longitudes 66°20′ to 97° east, measuring about 2000 miles from north to south and 1700 miles from east to west with a land area of about 1.27 million square miles or 811 million acres. The Tropic of Cancer roughly divides the country into two halves. India has a land frontier of about 8200 miles and a coast-line of about 3500 miles. Measured by the extent of territory, India is the seventh largest country in the world ; and is approximately thirteen times as large as the United Kingdom and eight times as large as Japan. The Union of India comprises 14 States (including the State of Jammu and Kashmir) and centrally administered territories.

2. The average annual rainfall in India is about 42 inches. But the distribution is very unequal, some areas getting abundant rainfall while some others getting not more than two or three inches per annum. West Bengal, Assam and the coastal strip towards the west of the western ghats get more than 80 inches of rainfall per year and the rest of the area of the country with the exception of desert regions of Rajasthan and Punjab gets varying rainfall ranging between 20 and 80 inches. Indian climate is markedly affected by monsoons, the South West monsoon being instrumental for 85 per cent of rainfall in the country. The temperature has little extremes except in the north where it ranges from 4°.4C to 46°.1C. The rest of the country is generally hot. Calcutta has a mean annual temperature of 26°.1C with a range from 10°C to 29°.4C. The mean temperature for Madras and Bombay are respectively 26°.7C but the annual ranges are of the order of ten degrees. The country has two important crop seasons, *kharif*

---

[1] Figures in millions (1951 census) of persons speaking : Hindi (105.64), Urdu (35.57), Hindustani (8.16), Telegu (33.00), Marathi (27.05), Tamil (26.55), Bengali (25.12), Gujrati (16.31), Kannada (14.47), Malayalam (13.38), Oriya (13.15), and Assamese (4.99). Three other languages have special recognition : Punjabi (0.27), Kashmiri (0.05) and Sanskrit.

[2] Figures in millions (1951 census) of religious denominations : Hindus (303.19), Sikhs (6.22), Jains (1.62), Buddhists (0.18), Zoroastrians (0.11), Muslims (35.40), Christians (8.16), Jews (0.03), Tribals (1.66) and Others (0.05).

or summer and *rabi* or winter ; as much as 80 per cent of cereal crops are produced in the *kharif* season and the rest in the *rabi* season.

3. India has the second biggest population in the world, 360 million in 1951 out of which roughly five-sixths belong to the rural areas. Roughly 48 per cent of the population is below 14 years while only about 8 per cent of the population is above 54. The crude birth rate is reported to be 4 per cent and the crude death rate is 2.7 per cent. Also there are 95 females to every hundred male in the country. Population has been increasing at a rate of over 1 per cent per year, i.e., with an annual net addition of about 4 or 4.5 million.[1] Compared to population the land area is small, and the share of land is only about 2 acres per head[2] against nearly 6 times this area in the USA and more than 12 times in the USSR. The average density of population in India is 312 per square mile ; it varies considerably from region to region and is as high as 832 per square mile in lower Gangetic plains. Per capita agricultural and arable land is roughly the same in India while the per capita agricultural land is more than twice the arable land in the USA.

4. Agriculture is the chief industry engaging about 70 per cent of working population. Out of every 100 employed Indians, 48 are mainly peasant proprietors including rentiers, 9 mainly tenants, 13 landless labourers, 10 engaged in industries or other non-agricultural production, 6 in commerce, 2 in transport and 12 in services and miscellaneous professions. There are certain difficulties associated with definition of labour force, particularly for the rural population, but roughly the labour force is likely to be between 40 to 45 per cent of the population of the country.

5. Agricultural products form nearly half of the net national output. Besides supplying raw materials to industries like sugar and textiles, it provides the bulk of the country's export. In the total geographical area of 811 million acres, about 300 million acres of net area are cultivated annually in India, the gross cultivated area being of the order of 350 million acres. Besides this, there exists about 60 to 70 million acres of fallow land. Roughly

---

[1] The recent rate of growth of population in India is not known accurately, but there are reasons to believe that it may be as high as 2 per cent. The rate observed over the period 1941 to 1951 was of the order of 1.2 per cent per year. It is worth noting that the growth of population in the UK between 1881-1951 was somewhat higher than this (i.e., 1.2 per cent). The rate of increase in population (by birth and migration) during the same period was still greater in the USA.

[2] Figures quoted without date indicate the general order of values in recent years.

220 million acres of land are reported to be not available for cultivation while about 130 million acres of land are under forests.
The main feature of agricultural production in India is the excess
of food crops (which occupy 85 per cent of the area sown) over
non-food crops. Cereals (rice, wheat, barley, *jowar*, *ragi*, *bajra*
and maize) form the staple food. India grows tea, coffee, sugarcane, oilseeds, jute and cotton, and other tropical crops including
fruits and vegetables ; tea and jute are important for export. India
is the largest sugarcane producing country of the world and with
Pakistan holds virtual monopoly in the production of jute. India
follows the USA in cotton and compares favourably with China
as a leading producer of rice, millets and tea. The most important
oilseed is groundnut. According to official estimates of production, the output of food grains is of the order of 65 million tons of
which rice contributes an amount of the order of 25 million tons. The
other important grains are wheat and *jowar*, between 8 and 10
million tons and gram and *bajra*, between 3 and 5 [million tons.
It is not possible to be absolutely sure of these figures, and there
is likelihood of some amount of underestimation. The cattle
population is very large being about 20 crores[1] in 1956. That
is, it is about half the size of the human population. The quality,
however, is poor and the supply of milk meagre. The average
yield of milk per cow per annum is only a little over 400 lbs., which
compares unfavourably with other countries in which the average
ranges between 2000 and 7000 lbs. Milk is consumed fluid or
converted into products such as *ghee* (clarified butter), *dahi* (curd),
khoa (dried milk), etc. Bulk of the milk is from buffaloes which
comprise a little more than one-fourth of the total population.
Dung is the most important manure used in the country and this
is one reason why the economic value of the cattle population is
more than what it appears on the surface. India's forests cover
280,000 square miles which is nearly 22 per cent of the total geographical area of the country yielding a government revenue worth
a little more than Rs. 20 crores annually[2]. Apart from timber
and bamboo, forests supply fuel wood, an essential item of domestic use. Fish provides an occasional item of diet for numerous
people in India and supplies useful protein. But the output is
not large, the total value being of the order of Rs. 50-60 crores.
The supply of food in India is adequate when the seasonal rainfall

---

[1] 1 crore=100 lakhs=10 million ; [2] Rs. 100=7.5 sterling= 21 US dollars.

is normal. There was, however, shortage of food for about ten years since 1942 which made it necessary to import foodgrains to the extent of 2 to 3 million tons per year for a number of years with the largest import of 4.7 million tons in 1951. The food position became easier from 1952, partly due to two or three years of exceptionally good crop seasons. However, there is still a somewhat precarious balance between the production of food and the requirements of the growing population unless one reckons on import of foodgrains.*

6. Agricultural land in India is basically fertile, though naturally suffering from different degrees of exhaustion from continuous use. This is particularly true of alluvial soil of north India. The black soil of Deccan as well as red and laterite soils found in other parts of India are also fertile and suitable for cultivation. About 45 per cent of the total area is under some kind of cultivation. As has been already mentioned, distribution of rainfall in the country is uneven and even a partial failure of monsoon results in famine conditions in some parts of the country. Irrigation, therefore, is very important for Indian agriculture. Of the total area under cultivation, about 17 per cent is under major and minor irrigation and the rest is dependent on rainfall. Out of the total irrigated area of about 55 million acres in 1954, canals accounted for about 22 million acres, wells 16 million acres, tanks 10 million acres and the rest 6 million acres. There is a large difference between the yield per acre on irrigated and on unirrigated lands; and irrigation normally raises production

---

* According to the 1951 census the population in the rural areas was roughly 300 million. There is a general impression that there is much surplus population in villages, but this is still an open question. It is possible that although the agricultural population is very large, it is needed to supply labour essential at the period of peak load (at the stage of transplantation of the rice crop, or at the stage of harvesting of rice and other crops). Some direct information on this point has been recently collected which suggests that there is sometimes shortage of agricultural labour at peak loads. This is also indicated by the seasonal movement of factory labour in some cities : a large number of labourers leave their factories to go back to their villages at certain periods of the year (peak load points of agriculture), and come back after finishing agricultural work. If one portion of the agricultural population is drawn away from the villages, there would be some decrease in the outturn of crops. If the decrease in the outturn of foodgrains due to such labour shortage is greater than the net contribution (i.e., total contribution minus consumption of food) of the transferred workers to the national income then obviously it would be economical, in a broad sense, to keep these labour households within the village to supply the peak load of labour required for full agriculture production, even if they do not have other gainful work during the rest of the year. On this view, there would be a biological balance between the size of the agricultural population and the volume of crop production, and it is conceivable that a decrease in agricultural population (without introducing labour saving devices) might diminish the real income per person. This question requires careful study.

from two to four times the original yield. India has a large number of big and small rivers and the quantity of water that annually flows along India's rivers is estimated at nearly 1400 million acre-feet. Of this volume of water only 5.6 per cent is used for irrigation works and power generation and the rest runs to waste. Irrigation schemes are being developed for a long time and recently a few big river valley schemes (irrigation and electricity) have been started and on completion, these are expected to irrigate 17 million acres of new land ; at this stage India will begin to use 13.6 per cent of her total river flow. There are still large possibilities of developing irrigation schemes. Moreover, there is much scope and need of developing minor irrigation works and water lifting devices for areas unsuitable for flow irrigation. In 1955 India produced 11,000 million kwh of electrical energy, giving a per capita figure of the order of 30 kwh. The corresponding figure in the USA is of the order of 2800, UK 1300 and Japan 650. Hydro-electricity accounts for roughly a little more than one-third of the energy generated in 1954, the rest being produced by the thermal stations.

7. India has the largest reserve of high quality iron ore in the world ; there are also fair reserves of coal, bauxite (for aluminium), monazite sand (for thorium), mica, chromite and refractories, some gold and copper and minor minerals. The iron reserves in the country are mostly haematites and magnetites with iron content ranging between 60 and 70 per cent ; India's total reserves have been estimated at 21,000 million metric tons and almost inexhaustible at the current rate of production. India ranks seventh among the coal-producing countries in the world and has an average annual production of about 36 million tons. The country has fairly abundant reserves of manganese ore and the present production is third largest in the world; the country has 15 to 20 million tons of good ore containing 50 per cent of the metal; moreover the Indian ore is non-friable and hence easily transportable. So far as bauxite is concerned, many of the laterites contain 50 to 80 per cent of aluminium ; the total reserve of bauxite in the country is estimated at 250 million tons. India has virtual monopoly of mica mining and produces 70 to 80 per cent of world's supply of mica. Small reserves of petrol have been found, but certain areas likely to bear oil have not yet been properly prospected. Geological surveys have made good progress but there has not been enough prospecting for minerals. In recent years, India

has been producing minerals worth about Rs. 100 crores, coal contributing roughly half of the total value. The other important minerals are manganese ore, mica, gold, salt, building materials and iron ore, the values in descending order ranging between Rs.20 to 30 crores.

8.   The net output of organized factories is comparatively small and accounts for less than 10 per cent of net material production. The net value added by factories (employing 10 or more persons with power, or, 20 or more persons without power) is only about 6 or 7 per cent of the national income. The number of factory workers is about 2.7 million which is only about two per cent of the total working force and about three-quarters of one per cent of the total population. The number of factories (in round figures) is about 30,000, of which about 25,000 are small and employ less than 100 persons ; 2500 factories employ more than 200 persons ; and only about a thousand factories are really big. The geographical distribution of factories and factory employment is very uneven. Most of these industries produce consumer goods and the largest single industry, cotton textiles roughly provides one-fourth of the employment in the factory industry sector. The production of basic investment goods (steel, cement, machinery), or of power (coal, electricity) is extremely low compared to the population. Output of producer goods, including coal and other minerals, is of the order of one-sixth of the total fabricated output. During the First Five Year Plan, the factory output increased by about 40 per cent ; of these capital goods exhibited a rise of 70 per cent while both consumer goods and intermediate goods rose by about 35 per cent. Though capital goods production increased more rapidly, the position is yet unsatisfactory because of the very low share of such goods in the base period. Excess capacity is still reported to exist in several of the consumer goods industries. The production of some important commodities in 1953-54 is given in Table 1 of the Plan-frame (reproduced in the Appendix).

9.   India is a country of small scale industries ; and only recently attention has been given to the development of large-scale industries. Indian economy is basically one of small household units of production ; and most of the enterprises are run by self-employed persons. Cottage industries offer alternative employment to the agricultural labourers. Very little accurate information is available on small-scale industries, but roughly it can be stated that the value of outupt in the sector is unlikely to be less than that

in the organized factories while the labour force engaged in the sector is somewhat more than four times that engaged in the organized sector. Handloom weaving is by far the most important small-scale industry supplying a sizable part of the need of textiles in the country and providing employment for a large number of artisans. The industries are of varied types, ranging from units specializing in goods of artistic value to units carrying on operations using modern technique to some extent.

10. There is a nationalized system of railways (with about 34,000 miles of tracks) which is the principal means of transport in the country. There is roughly 250,000 miles of extra-municipal roads in India of which the share of surfaced roads is not even 4 per cent. The length of all weather roads is only 9.7 miles per hundred square miles of the area of the country, and is very low compared to the population. The number of registered motor vehicles in 1950-51 was only 308,002. India has a 3500 miles long coast line with five major ports. Indian coastal shipping is at present nearly 300,000 gross rated tons ; and practically the whole of the coastal trade is now carried by Indian ships. Air services have been established to link important cities ; and a nationalized air transport system is in existence. India possesses 800 registered aircrafts of which about 200 hold current certificates of air-worthiness. The country has 78 aerodromes of which three are international. There is an old and well-established system of posts and telegraphs. The total number of post offices is 6000 in urban and nearly 30,000 in rural areas. The expansion of postal network has kept pace with the growth of population in recent years. The telegraph network is inadequate with about 8000 telegraph offices only. India is very backward in the field of telephones ; it is even more backward than China. The total number of telephone lines within the country is even less than that in one city of Australia, viz. Sidney. Thus, transport and communication have a good base but are extremely inadequate.

11. Commerce plays an important part in the Indian economy and the labour force engaged in commercial activities is roughly three times the labour force in organized factories ; the total industrial labour force, however, is about 50 per cent above the labour force in commercial activities, and the net output of commerce is somewhat below the net output of the industries. Bulk of the trading in India is handled by small retailers including hawkers, and small wholesalers ; but organized trading plays an important

role in the Indian economy. Organized traders pay much more income tax than organized industries. Banking also has two sectors : the organized banking with Reserve Bank of India and the State Bank at the apex and the unorganized banking including rural money lenders who play a very important role in production and distribution. There are cooperative banks also, but on the whole the development of cooperation has been inadequate in India ; the most important type of primary institution is the credit society which numbers only about 1.4 lakhs and has a membership of 6.6 million. Insurance in India generally does not cater to the poorest of the classes. Recently, insurance has been nationalized and it may have a wider spread in the future.

12. Educational facilities are meagre compared to the population; there is provision of schools for only 50 per cent of the children of the age group 6-11 ; 17 per cent of the children of the age group 11-14 ; 8 per cent in the age group 14-17 ; and less than one (0.9) per cent of those of the age group 17-23. Only about 17 per cent of the population is literate, about 12 per cent in rural areas and about 35 per cent in urban areas. Moreover, there are great differences in educational facilities in different States or in urban and rural areas. Though nearly 82 per cent of the population live in the rural areas the percentages of total number of students in primary, middle and high schools studying in rural areas are roughly about 60, 67 and 26 respectively in 1949-50. Also, nearly 40 per cent of total number of teachers in primary and middle schools are untrained. Some 380,000 students pass matriculation or an equivalent examination each year, and there has been remarkable growth in this number in recent times. Number of students in some 30 universities and 680 colleges is less than 3 lakhs. There is very little facility for technical and vocational education in the country. There are some 2750 vocational schools, 42 engineering schools and about an equal number of engineering colleges. There are about 20,000 pupils in engineering schools and 16,000 pupils in engineering colleges. Annual outturn is about 2500 engineers from colleges.

13. The average expectation of life is only about 35 years compared to 75 years in the USA and a little over 70 in the UK while infantile mortality per 1000 live births is as high as 130 in India against 30 in the USA and in the UK. Deaths caused by epidemic diseases form nearly 50 per cent of the total mortality. The prevalence of diseases, like malaria and tuberculosis is very

high and cause deaths to more than one million persons every year. The number of medical personnel is extremely low. There are only about 65,000 fully qualified (six-year trained) doctors with an overall share of one doctor for about 6000 persons (against about one per 1000 persons in the UK). But the distribution is extremely uneven, only about one-fourth, that is, 15 or 16 thousand doctors live in rural areas with a share of only one doctor for about 20,000 villagers. In some States the proportion is much less. Nurses, health visitors and other auxiliary health and medical personnel are proportionately even fewer in number. Medical institutions are very few ; one for about 25,000 persons in the urban area and one for 50,000 persons in rural areas. The availability of beds is only one per 3000 persons, but again mostly in urban areas. There are about 40 medical colleges now with an annual admission of about 3500 pupils.

14. Not much statistical data are available on the various other social and public services. The most important of these in the recent past was perhaps the problem of rehabilitation of refugees from Pakistan. The problem is now considered to be under control, though there is still influx of refugees from East Pakistan and this is a case of continual worry of the Central and West Bengal governments. The position of housing in the country, particularly in the urban areas is far from satisfactory and requires regular attention of the government. Other important services which requires attention are welfare of the backward classes and welfare of labourers. Prohibition has been accepted as a policy of the Congress Party, and some of the States have given effect to the policy in spite of its adverse effect on government revenue. Recently, attention is being paid towards reform of government administrative services so as to make the services more suitable for purposes of planning. The press with 330 newspapers and a circulation of dailies totalling only 25 lakhs reaches a small fraction of the population. More than 300 feature films and documentaries are produced each year and there are about 1 million radio receiving sets.

15. The problem of land reform has received considerable attention in recent years ; and measures of land reform have practically eliminated or will soon eliminate intermediate rights on land in most of the States. Except in Jammu and Kashmir, compensation on a sliding scale is being paid to intermediaries who are losing their rights on land. In many cases the maximum rent

3

to be charged as well as the maximum size of holding have been prescribed ; most of the States have fixed 30 standard acres as the ceiling of holdings. Some attention is being paid to prevent further fragmentation of holding due to operation of laws of inheritance and also to consolidate the holdings on a voluntary and cooperative basis. Most of the States are putting restriction on partition or transfer below specified limits and are adopting legislation for consolidation of holdings. The average size of ownership holdings is very small and less than 5 acres in rural areas. The distribution of rural land is, however, very uneven. About a fifth of rural households have no land. About half either have no land or own less than one or one and a half acre, and their total share is only about two per cent of the total area owned by rural households. At the upper end about 10 per cent of households have more than 10 or 12 acres, and own about 60 per cent of the land.

16. The consideration of various sectors of the economy may be followed by some observations on the aggregates. A rough idea about the general pattern of the total value produced is provided by the following : investment about 5 per cent ; public consumption 4 per cent ; and private consumption 64 per cent ; the rest of the product enters intermediate uses. Investment at the present moment is estimated at a little below 7 per cent of the net national product, but roughly one-fifth of this is in non-monetized activities such as land improvement and construction of huts in rural areas. Public investment (net) in recent times has moved roughly from one third to half of the total investment. In the organized private sector, most of the fixed investment is in industry and mining, the second most important sector being transport. But investment in industry and transport put together is less than the investment in urban construction. Very little is known about investments in inventories in the private sector. There is not much barter but a large part of the economy (may be something like 30 or 35 per cent of the whole) is non-monetory, with a large volume of home consumption of home produced food and other goods. The national income was about Rs. 28 per month per person ; and an expenditure in cash, on an average, probably of only about Rs. 17 or Rs. 18 per month per person. A small number of households are very rich. Only about 5 lakh (half a million) pay income tax with an exemption limit of Rs. 2,500 per year. There is a large number of very poor people ; about one

eighth of the population (or about 50 million) probably have less than 10 rupees (i.e., 15 shillings or about 2 US dollars) per month per person.

17. While agriculture and allied pursuits (animal husbandry, forestry and fishery) roughly contributes a little less than half of the national income, the remaining half is shared more or less equally by mining and industries, commerce and transport, and various services. There has been some rise in national income in recent times ; in particular rises in agriculture, organized industries and in some of the service sectors have been quite pronounced, but a part of the apparent rise may probably be due to statistical adjustments. It is not clearly known how far the estimates of national income from year to year truly reflect the underlying change. But accepting the figures as they are, a large rise in per capita national income is noticed between 1950-51 and 1953-54 ; subsequently the evidence is indicative of just a maintenance of the per capita level reached in 1953-54.

18. Consumption pattern in the country is different in different regions ; also there is marked difference between urban and rural areas. Roughly two-thirds of the consumer expenditure in rural areas are on food ; in urban areas, the percentage is of the order of 55. Again some 40 per cent of rural expenditure is on foodgrains, while the corresponding figure for urban area is a little above 20 per cent. In so far as meat, fish and eggs are concerned, the rural families spend 2 per cent on these items while the urban families spend 3 per cent. Regarding clothing and milk and milk products, the relative share in urban areas is only slightly above that in rural areas and in respect of fuel and light the percentage is more or less the same. The residual group, of course, is considerably higher in urban areas than in the rural areas. The pattern of expenditures also naturally varies with the per capita expenditure level of the household. Thus, both in urban and rural areas, the share of expenditure on food is about 70 per cent in the per capita expenditure class below Rs. 8 per month and of the order of 40 per cent in the per capita expenditure class above Rs. 55 per month.

19. There is a good deal of unemployment. Many persons are without jobs and many self employed persons do not have enough gainful work in hand. During the last two or three years unemployment in the urban areas has been increasing. The visible unemployment in urban areas may have reached two or three million in 1954. The corresponding figure in the rural areas may

be of the same order, that is, the pool of visible unemployment may be something of the order of 4 or 5 million. There are also fresh additions to the labour force every year. The age structure of the population is fairly stable and as the proportion of the working force is between 40 per cent and 45 per cent, and as the population is growing by something like 4 or 4.5 million every year it follows that about 1.8 million persons would enter the working force every year. Unless sufficient new work is created to absorb these new entrants into the labour force the number of unemployed persons would go on increasing continually. Besides visible unemployment in respect of paid jobs there is a great deal of underemployment or disguised unemployment. Many agricultural labourers or artisans and craftsmen do not have enough work and remain idle for a considerable part of the year. There are conceptual difficulties in giving definite figures. Various estimates have been made ranging from 10 or 12 million to over 30 million in terms of equivalent man years. It is beyond dispute that a very large number of people are often obliged to remain idle for lack of work. For both social and political reasons unemployment is the most pressing problem in India today.

20. On the credit side India has a stable Government with wise leadership, a stable currency credit-worthy at the international level; a fairly stable foreign trade, fairly good Government machinery for law and order and for routine administration; a number of universities, scientific institutions and societies; and a nucleus of experienced scientists and technologists.

21. There has been some notable progress during the First Five Year Plan. Some large river valley schemes for irrigation and power have started coming into operation; the area irrigated have gone up by about 6 per cent and power generated has gone up by two thirds. Some completely modern factories in the public sector have started working and mention may be made of Hindustan Shipyards, Hindustan Machine Tools, Sindri Fertilizer Factory, Hindustan Antibiotics, Hindustan Cables, Hindustan Insecticides, Chittaranjan Locomotives, Indian Telephone Industries and Integral Coach Factory in this connection. All the above enterprises are central; some of the State Governments also started new factories. Further, three steel plants are under construction under the auspices of the Central Government. The progress in the private sector has already noted to be satisfactory, the overall index number of industrial production moving up by about 40 per cent

over the plan period. A big scheme of Community Projects and National Extension Service Blocks has been initiated in the rural areas which may develop into an important movement to revolutionize rural economy. Upto 1955-56, work has started in almost a thousand Community Project and National Extension Service Blocks covering a population of a little less than 9 crores. The services are expected to encompass the whole of the rural population during the Second Plan. The area sown has gone up by more than 7 per cent while the index number of agricultural production is roughly 20 per cent above the pre-plan periods. The level of foreign trade has not changed materially over the plan period, but the volume of internal trade has increased. Prices exhibited a declining trend after the post Korean war boom in 1951-52 in spite of some deficit spending by the government towards the end of the plan period ; the rate of decline has not been so large as to cause worry. Inland passenger transport remained steady, but the railway goods transport increased by as much as 35 per cent. Education flourished in so far as quantitative aspect is concerned, about 70 per cent more students graduated or passed higher examinations in 1954-55 in comparison with 1950-51, while the corresponding percentage is about 60 for matriculation and equivalent examinations. Further, 14 National Laboratories for scientific and technological research have been established. The progress in health services has not been so large. Also, employment flagged behind and created difficult situations in urban areas. Industrial employment went up by only 5 per cent, employment in railway by 10 per cent while the Central Government services expanded by 12 per cent over a period in which the national product reportedly increased by 18 per cent. But quite apart from the question of material progress, the greatest achievement of the First Five Year Plan has been that it made the whole country Plan-conscious. Increased interest is being taken by the general public in economic conditions and problems ; and great expectations have been roused about the Second Five Year Plan.

CHAPTER 3

THE GENERAL APPROACH OF THE PLAN-FRAME

THE PROBLEM OF UNEMPLOYMENT

1. The chief aim of planning in India, in the first instance, must be to solve the problem of unemployment as quickly as possible. In India we have vast resources of iron ore, coal, and other minerals; large possibilities of developing river valley (hydro-electric and irrigation) projects; raw materials of many kinds; and yet there are millions of people either without jobs, or sitting partly idle. The obvious reason is the great shortage of capital goods. In highly industrialized countries there is full employment (with potential shortage of labour) when the economy is working at full capacity. Unemployment can occur only when means of production remain idle. The situation in India is different. Unemployment is chronic because of lack of capital goods. The only way of eliminating unemployment in India is to build up a sufficiently large stock of capital which will enable all unemployed persons being absorbed into productive activity. Increasing the rate of investment is, therefore, the only fundamental remedy for unemployment in India.

SMALL SCALE AND HOUSEHOLD INDUSTRIES

2. In the highly industrialized countries, under conditions of full employment, the rate of investment can be increased only by curtailing consumption. In India the general level of consumption is extremely low. Some savings no doubt can be created by reducing consumption in certain sectors but the scope is small. We have, however, idle man-power and raw materials. It is logical, therefore, to think of expanding the production in the small scale and household industries. This sector is capital-light and labour-intensive. We have a long tradition of handicrafts in India. We know how to manufacture the tools and means of production for the small scale and household industries. A comparatively small amount of capital could generate a large volume of employment and could also supply much additional consumer goods for sale. During the war (1940-45) we witnessed a large expansion of small scale and household production in response to the increasing demand

for goods. If we can increase the demand, it should be again possible to increase the production in the small and household industries.

3. How can this be done ? In two different ways. Any increase of investment in the heavy industries producing investment goods (which do not compete with the small and household industries) must create new purchasing power and hence generate new demand. The effect will be the same if we increase expenditure on health, education, and other social services (which also do not compete with the small and household industries). It is clear, therefore, that the basic strategy of planning in India should be, on one hand, to increase investments in the heavy industries and also expenditure on services to increase purchasing power and create fresh demand; and, on the other hand, to increase the supply of consumer goods by increasing investment and production as much as possible in the small and household industries to meet the new demand. In India the correct policy is to increase both consumption and investment at the same time.

4. Until unemployment is brought under control there should not be, therefore, any fresh investments to expand factories which compete with the small and household units of production. In addition, in special cases, it may be also necessary to impose a temporary ban on further expansion of factory production which is competitive with small scale or hand production. This may result in some surplus factory capacity remaining idle temporarily. It may be better to allow machines to remain idle rather than to keep human beings unemployed.

5. The price of hand-made goods would be sometimes higher than the price of factory-made goods of comparable quality. A simple remedy is to levy suitable excise duties on factory-made goods to preserve price parity with hand-made goods at any desired level. This would, no doubt, raise prices to some extent but would at the same time supply additional resources for investment and hence for additional employment, increase of income, and national development.

6. Under planning, the whole economy would be continually expanding. Income and consumption would increase. The unemployed would get more and more absorbed in productive activity. The self-employed, the household sector, and the poorer sections would gain relatively more than the richer sections of the population. The poorer people would not mind paying somewhat higher prices (which would flow back into the hands of Government

as additional resources for development), once they realize that this is the inescapable condition for their own prosperity. Any person who has no employment or whose earning is low at present would prefer to have work or to increase his earning even if this means that a part of the increase in income would go back to Government in the form of additional tax or higher prices. It cannot satisfy a person without employment to know that prices will remain low but he would not be able to make any purchases for lack of money. He would prefer the opportunity to earn something with which to purchase what he wants even if this means that he would have to pay somewhat higher prices.

7. It would be wise to give the highest priority to the elimination of unemployment; and to try to decide the basic approach for the Second Five Year Plan with the object of reaching full employment in 10 years or less.* The above formulation of the problem implies, of course, that after getting rid of unemployment it would be necessary to maintain full employment in future. As population in India is growing steadily it is necessary to create enough new work and employment every year to absorb the new entrants into the labour force. That is, in India employment must expand at least as fast as the population which requires that the national economy must also expand, at least, equally fast.

8. We must thus look beyond 5 or 10 years; and have a "perspective" of 20 or 30 years or even more (although the programme or plan would necessarily have to be worked out in the concrete for 5 or 10 years and even year by year in the light of experience). The aim would be to increase the national income as much as possidle while progressing towards full employment, and to continue to increase national income after reaching full employment. This is the logical basis of the two objectives of . (a) increasing employment and (b) attaining a satisfactory rate of increase of income which have been adopted in the Plan-frame.

---

* In a "fully socialized" economy, maximizing national income would be a sufficient condition as this would enable maximizing employment at the same time because a part of the increase in income can be distributed in a suitable way to create a large volume of employment or provide appropriate benefits to the unemployed. (For example, both children and adults can even be paid for attending schools or clinics). In an "unplanned" economy, maximizing profits or income might lead to an increase in unemployment. In highly industrialized countries such temporary unemployment can be taken care of through unemployment insurance and social services. This is not possible in an under-developed country like India where, under mixed economy, it seems preferable to state the aim of (partial) planning as the attainment of full employment (and not simply the maximization of the rate of growth of income).

9. In the present approach great emphasis has been given to building up quickly the basic heavy industries. This would lay a sound foundation for the manufacture of machinery which would improve the efficiency of industrial production in future. As the problem of unemployment comes under control and as the basic industries are gradually developed, modern machinery would be supplied in increasing quantities to the small and household industries; and factory production of consumer goods would also be expanded as necessary to lead to a continually increasing level of living. In India, the wise policy would be to disperse production as much as possible, physically, in the sense of preference being given to the smallest units of production which are economical from a national point of view, and also geographically.

BASIC HEAVY INDUSTRIES

10. I may now consider the question of economic development over a long period of time. Although production can be increased to some extent by utilizing idle capacity, by working double or triple shifts, or by increasing the skill of the worker, the long-term growth of the economy will depend on the rate of increase of the means of production, that is, on the rate of increase of investment.

11. Econometric "models" are particularly useful for the study of long period growth. The art of model building lies in selecting a small number of significant factors (out of the innumerable factors affecting the economy) and putting these simple factors in a definite relationship to constitute a "model" which would serve as a representative substitute for reality. A study of the changes in the model would then supply some idea of the real process of growth. The usefulness of the "model" would, of course, depend on the extent to which the model succeeds in representing reality in the essential features under study.

12. Since 1950 we have been studying simple models of the relation between increase in the national income and amount of new investments over a long period of time in the USA, UK and some other countries. On the basis of these studies (Mahalanobis, 1952) I had reached the conclusion that the rate of investment in India must be increased to 10 or 11 per cent in order to attain a satisfactory rate of expansion of the national economy. Since then further studies were made (to which more detailed reference is made in a later chapter) on the basis of which we found that,

4

under planning, the ratio of the increase of the national income
to new investments may be reasonably expected to be about 0.5
in India.   If we aim at an increase of income of about 5 per cent
per year (which would double the national income in about 14
years and the per capita income in about 18 years) then it would
be necessary to increase the average rate of investment to about
10 or 11 per cent per year.   As the national income of India is of
the order of ten or eleven thousand crores of rupees, in order to
increase the national income by 5 per cent per year or by something like 27 per cent in 5 years, the total capital requirement
would be something between, say, five and six thousand crores
of rupees spread over 5 years.   Besides investments, there would
also be some developmental expenditure on training and social
programmes.   Allowing about one thousand crore for such purposes the "size" of the plan, as measured by the financial outlay,
should be something between six and seven thousand crores in
5 years.   This is a convenient starting point.

13.   The rate of development over a long period is, however,
intimately connected with the pattern of investment.   For example,
if all investments are made in industries producing consumer goods
(by importing capital goods from abroad) then there would be, no
doubt, a good deal of increase in the immediate supply of consumer
goods but there would be no increase in the capacity to manufacture
capital goods in India so that we shall have to continue to depend
on the import of foreign machinery in future for further expansion
of industries.   There may also be a glut of consumer goods (as has
happened in India from time to time) followed by unemployment.

14.   India has plenty of iron ore, coal and other natural resources.
The long-term aim should, therefore, be to manufacture capital
goods within the country rather than to import them.   The proper
strategy would be to bring about a rapid development of the industries producing investment goods in the beginning by increasing
appreciably the proportion of investment in the basic heavy industries.   As the capacity to manufacture both heavy and light
machinery and other capital goods increases, the capacity to invest
(by using home-produced capital goods) would also increase steadily
and India would become more and more independent of the import
of foreign machinery and capital goods.

15.   Some illustrative figures may be useful.   Indian reserves
of iron ore have been estimated at about 21,000 million metric
tons which is just one-fourth of the total reserves of the whole

world and more than three times bigger than the estimated reserves
of the USA (less than 7,000 million metric tons), or more than
five times that of the UK (4,000 million metric tons, UN Report,
1955). Indian ore has a high iron content. India also
has coal. The production of steel in India in 1954 was about 1.2
million tons for a population of possibly 375 or 380 million persons
against about 110 million tons for a population of 165 million
in the USA and about 20 million tons for a population of 50 million
in the UK. Compared to India, the production of steel per person
is more than two hundred times higher in the USA and more than
hundred times greater in the UK.

16. More steel per person means more machinery per person;
and more machinery means more production per person. The
difference in the level of living in these three countries can be easily
explained by the differences in the rate of production of steel.
For a single factor, the production of steel probably has the highest
correlation with national income in different countries.[1]

17. The production of steel must be progressively increased
in India. It has been decided that three new million-ton steel
plants would be installed during the Second Five Year Plan or as
soon as possible. Each new million-ton steel plant involves an
investment of about Rs. 100 crores (£75 million sterling or 200
million US dollars) in round numbers. Out of this amount about
Rs. 45 crores (£34 million sterling or 90 million US dollars) would
have to be spent in foreign currency to import machinery made
mostly of steel. It has been proposed in the Plan-frame that a
heavy machine building industry should be established in India
so that as soon as possible India is able to fabricate machinery
for the production of steel (or cement or capital goods) to
the value of say Rs. 40 or Rs. 50 crores per year. Once this is done
it would be possible to develop steel and other basic industries
with the help of our own resources.[2] The ratio of capital to gross

---

[1] From some preliminary studies it appears that the coefficient of correlation
between per capita production of steel and per capita national income is so high
as $+0.75$ for a group of 19 countries in 1953 for which data were available.

[2] It is not necessary that India should manufacture everything required for
the installation of a steel plant. In the case of machinery for the production of
steel there has been much specialization and even industrially advanced countries
(like the USA, the UK, or Germany) make considerable purchases from other
countries. But they also sell some of their own specialized products so that they
do not have to depend on foreign currency or loans. Furthermore, if there is any
difficulty in securing capital goods from abroad, they can start manufacturing
such goods to meet their own essential needs. It is most desirable that India
should attain a similar position as quickly as possible.

value of product is roughly 3 to 1 or somewhat less for the production of steel. On the same basis, the capital required to manufacture heavy machinery worth, say, Rs. 50 crores per year would be about Rs. 150 crores. Even if the heavy machine building industry is more capital-intensive than steel, the total capital required is not likely to exceed Rs. 200 crores; and the value of imported machinery required for this purpose cannot be higher than, say, Rs. 100 crores or Rs. 120 crores. The saving in foreign currency (in imports) for a single million ton steel factory would be about Rs. 40 or Rs. 45 crores. The foreign currency required to establish a heavy machine building industry would be recovered by the time three new million ton steel plants are installed with the help of home-produced machinery. If it is known that at least three new million ton steel plants would be installed *after* the establishment of the heavy machine building industry then there would be no risk in the decision to establish such an industry. Under planning there cannot be any doubt that India should produce 10 or 20 or 50 million tons or more of steel as soon as possible. Under planning it is, therefore, a safe and wise decision to establish a heavy machine building industry at the earliest opportunity.

18. I may give another example. India is believed to be short of copper but has large reserves of bauxite from which aluminium can be produced. The present consumption of aluminium is only 7 or 8 thousand tons per year, about half of which is produced in India and about half is imported. India is rapidly developing electricity for which large quantities of copper would have to be imported. The Plan-frame has recommended that the production of aluminium should be progressively increased with a view to replacing copper by aluminium to the largest extent possible. This would be a wise decision because it would increase production through the utilization of Indian resources; and would also make India progressively independent of imports of copper in future. This is the kind of thinking which made us give so much emphasis to the rapid development of the basic industries.*

---

* A rapid development of basic heavy industries which requires a great deal of capital can be brought about in India only through planning at a national level. A heavy machine building industry at a capital cost of Rs. 150 or Rs. 200 crores can be started only if there are reasonable prospects that new factories for the production of steel or other capital goods would continue to be established in sufficient numbers in future. It is Government alone which can make decisions about the rate and pattern of industrialization in future and hence can make the decision to establish the heavy machine building industry on a sufficiently large

19. At the same time we also examined the question from a more aggregative (or macroscopic) point of view. Studies based on a statistical model (discussed later) showed that the larger the share of capital goods industries in the total investment the larger would be the increase in the national income over a long period of time (of the order of 15 or 20 or 30 years) and the smaller will be the immediate rise. From the point of view of long range development it will be desirable to increase, as much as possible, the proportion of investment in the basic industries producing capital goods. There is, however, a physical and/or socially acceptable limit beyond which it is not possible to push up investments in the capital goods industries (because of the shortage of capital goods and technical personnel or because it would involve too great a sacrifice of immediate benefits).

BALANCE OF DEMAND AND SUPPLY

20. There is a second point. We think it would be desirable to avoid inflationary pressures as much as possible so that it would not be necessary to continue indefinitely the rationing of essential goods. The only way to achieve this is by balancing the supply and demand of essential goods. Investments in basic industries must not be pushed above a point beyond which the increase in demand caused by the increase in purchasing power cannot be absorbed by the additional production of consumer goods. This condition has been emphasized in the Plan-frame.

ALLOCATION OF RESOURCES

21. What should be the proportion of total investment to be allocated to the industries producing capital goods is the most crucial decision in perspective or long range planning. Once the choice is made of the share of investment in capital goods industries, the availability of capital goods in future years would become more or less determined. The only change which could be made would be through import (or export) of capital goods. From certain studies based on the model of 1953 we reached the conclusion that something between 30 per cent and 35 per cent of the total

---

scale to make it possible to instal, say, one new million ton steel plant every year in future. Inspite of the unrivalled natural resources for the production of steel in this country, in the absence of planning, India was producing only about one million ton per year up to 1953 and no action has been taken so far to manufacture heavy machinery. This clearly demonstrates how development was retarded for lack of planning in India.

investment should go to the industries producing capital goods. In India the present proportion is probably less than 10 per cent. In our view this proportion should be increased by three or four times.

22. Having settled the share of investment for the capital goods industries, broadly from considerations of long period development, the next step would be to decide the detailed allocation of investments to individual industries and services. At this stage attention must be given to the need of creating as much employment as possible. We have found it useful to use three sets of contingent parameters in considering different possibilities. We are interested firstly, in the ratio of the increase in output (in physical terms or in money value) to new investment, that is, the output per unit of new investment or the output coefficient of capital; secondly, in the ratio of the increase in net value added to new investment, that is, increase in income per unit of new investment, or the income coefficient of capital (which we have called β); and, thirdly, in the ratio of investment to the number of persons employed, that is, the amount of capital required per worker or the capital coefficient of labour (which we have called θ). Detailed studies are being made about these technological parameters for individual industries and groups of industries.

23. The technical methods used in the Plan-frame can be now briefly explained. The total amount of investment available having been provisionally settled, we may proceed (provisionally, of course) to distribute the investment to groups of industries or to individual industries and services. In each industry (or group of industries) the amount of investment having been (provisionally) settled, it would be possible (with the help of the technological coefficients mentioned above) to estimate the expected output in physical terms and in money value, the expected contribution to national income, and the expected volume of employment generated. Adding these up we can get the total income and employment which may be reasonably expected to be generated by any particular way of allocation of investments.

24. The physical targets of production, investment, income, and employment are thus completely interlocked. Not only this, there are also physical relations between quantities of material and labour required for the production of different commodities. The targets of production are, therefore, directly connected and interlocked among themselves through physical and technological relations.

25. There is also the question of meeting the expected increase in demand for consumer goods. A great deal of material on family budgets has been (and is being continually) collected since 1950 through the National Sample Survey. It is possible, therefore, to study the differences in the pattern of consumption among households at different levels of per capita (or per household) expenditure. Engel coefficients of elasticity are being studied for this purpose; and provisional values have been calculated for food grains, cloth, sugar and some other commodities. If we assume that households, when their income is increased, would incur expenditure (on an average) in the same way as households who at present have higher incomes are actually doing, that is, if we assume that tastes and preferences would remain (on an average) fairly stable, then it is possible to use the Engel coefficients of elasticity to estimate the increase in demand for individual commodities which is likely to occur as income increases. It is, of course, possible to make such estimates separately for different geographical regions, or for different occupational groups. In principle, it is thus possible to take into consideration the effect on demand not only of changes in income but also of changes in the rural and urban or occupational or regional distribution of population, or changes in the distribution by size of income.

26. For any particular allocation of investments to individual (or groups of) industries and services, it is, therefore, possible in principle to estimate the expected output of commodities, the expected increase in income, the expected increase in employment, and also the expected increase in demand. It is then possible to check whether there is a balance between requirements and supply of raw materials and labour at each stage of production; or whether there is a balance of supply and demand of consumer goods and services. If there is any lack of balance, then the targets must be suitably changed remembering that, in principle, a change in any single item may affect the other items. The balances must be then again checked. The whole process will have to be repeated until a set of physical targets with associated investments, income, and employment is reached which is internally consistent and in which the supply and demand is balanced at every stage of production and consumption.*

---

* It would not be possible to meet the demand for luxury goods and services as large resources cannot be permitted to be diverted to the production of luxury goods. A balance must be brought about through an appropriate price policy

27. It is possible to use some mathematical short cuts in making
the above calculations. For example, in principle, it is possible
to use advanced methods of linear and convex programming. A
number of Working Papers on this subject were prepared under
the leadership of Professor Ragnar Frisch of Oslo who worked
in the Indian Statistical Institute in the winter season of 1954-55.
Some of these papers have been printed. These refined methods
are extremely powerful but, unfortunately, it is not possible to use
them in the immediate future in India for lack of detailed data
which would be required for this purpose. In the meantime the
simpler methods described in Chapter 4 have been used for the
preparation of the Draft Plan-frame.

FIVE LIMITING FACTORS

28. The aim of planning in India must be to obtain the maximum
possible rate of increase of employment and national income over
a given time period. Planning must, therefore, maintain a wide
perspective of the growth of the national economy over 10, 20 or
30 years or more; and, at the same time, give adequate attention
to the urgent need of eliminating unemployment as quickly as
possible.

29. In the present approach, the strategy is to balance the
increase in demand created by investments in the heavy capital-
intensive industries and expenditure on services by adequate production of consumer goods at first through small and household
industries. The rate of development, if inflation is to be avoided,
would be determined by the amount of surplus consumer goods
which can be actually produced. The production of enough
consumer goods in the small and household industries is,
therefore, of strategic importance and may constitute a limiting
factor.

30. The capacity to invest (without import of capital goods)
in any given year is determined by the pattern and volume of production of capital goods in the previous year. The rate of expansion of the basic industries, therefore, sets a limit to the rate of
growth of the economy as a whole and may constitute a second
limiting factor.

(through the imposition, for example, of excise duties) or suitable fiscal measures.
There is no danger of inflation if the supply and demand can be balanced in the
case of essential commodities used by all sections of the people (such as cereals,
cloth, sugar).

31. The capacity to increase both production and the flow of services would depend on the rate at which technical personnel of the required type can be trained. Lack of trained personnel may be a serious bottleneck. The rate at which training can be provided would thus constitute a third limiting factor.

32. The possibility of planning on the proposed scale would depend on raising adequate financial resources which may constitute a fourth limiting factor. This, no doubt, involves technical questions of monetary and financial policy; but ultimately the basic decisions must be made on broad social and political considerations.

33. Finally, as pointed out in the Plan-frame, even if adequate financial resources can be raised, implementation may become difficult or impossible owing to rigidities in the existing system of administration. There must be thorough decentralization of administrative and financial powers in the case of public enterprises and institutions; and also active cooperation between official and non-official agencies. Inadequate administrative machinery may form a fifth limiting factor.

34. We are aware of these difficulties. The logical consistency of the Plan-frame is not a sufficient guarantee of its feasibility in practice. Any one (or two or more in combination) of the five limiting factors mentioned above can retard progress. However, so far as plan-making is concerned (as distinguished from plan-implementation) all that can be demanded is internal consistency, valid technical reasoning and a correct appreciation of social needs. If the present plan has these merits then there is only one single issue, namely, whether there is any alternative plan which would eliminate unemployment and poverty more quickly and more effectively; and at the same time, lay the foundations for a continuing increase in the level of living in future. If there is no alternative plan which is more satisfactory, then the proper policy would be to try to implement the present plan.

CHAPTER 4

THE STATISTICAL BASIS OF THE PLAN-FRAME

1. I shall now explain the statistical basis of the Draft Plan-frame. It will be useful to start with a brief recapitulation of some previous work. In 1949-50, I worked with a simple model covering the whole economy, that is, using one single sector for the national economy.[1] I used the ratio of the gross value of the additional product to the new investment required to generate this product; and adopting a value of unity for this ratio gave some estimates of the investment required per person to increase the level of living under Indian conditions.

SINGLE SECTOR MODEL

2. In 1951 and 1952, I worked with another model[2] for the whole economy in which I used the ratio of the increase in net national income per unit of time to the net investment associated with this additional income. I called this ratio β (which is the inverse of the marginal capital coefficient). If α is the rate of *net* investment, that is, the fraction of net national income used for investment, then the rate of growth of the economy is $\alpha\beta$. If ρ is the rate of increase of population (usually less than 2 per cent per annum), then the rate of increase of income per person is $(\alpha\beta - \rho)$ approximately.

3. From direct calculations I had found from the national income data for USA given by S. Kuznets (1946) that the value of β for USA was about one-third. I also found by direct calculations from data of national income and investment for UK given respetively by A. R. Prest (1948) and by J. H. Lenfant (1951) that the value of β for UK was something like one-fourth or a little smaller. I had also made some tentative calculations for Switzerland, Norway and some other countries from which I inferred that the value of β for the USA and some of the West European countries would

---

1 P. C. Mahalanobis : "Why Statistics ?" Presidential Address to the Indian Science Congress Association, Poona, 1950.

2 P. C. Mahalanobis : "National income, investment, and national development" (Lecture, National Institute of Sciences, 1952). The model I used is similar to the models used a little earlier by Harrod and by Domar but I did not know of their work at the time of writing.

probably fall between one-fifth and one-third (that is, the over-all marginal capital coefficient would be something between 5 and 3). Using similar values of β for India I reached the conclusion that it would be necessary to increase the rate of investment in India from about 5 per cent at the time to at least 10 or 11 per cent to attain a reasonably satisfactory rate of increase of national income.

Two-Sector Model

4. I used a two-sector model in 1953 which I shall now briefly describe.[1] The total net investment is divided into two portions. One part (a fraction, say, λ_k) is used to increase the production of basic capital or investment goods (which may be called the K-sector), and the other part (a fraction, say λ_c) is used to increase the production of consumer goods (to be called the C-sector). It should be noted that λ_k and λ_c are fractions of the total investment, so that $\lambda_k + \lambda_c = 1$. I should also explain that appropriate fractions of investments in industries manufacturing intermediate (producer) goods should be allocated to λ_k and to λ_c in proportion to the value of such intermediate goods used in the capital goods (K-sector) and the consumer goods (C-sector) industries respectively. The two fractions λ_k and λ_c can be settled at the choice of the planners. However, once the value of λ_k is settled, the supply of investment goods produced within the country would become fixed. A change can be brought about only through imports or exports of investment goods. In India I have assumed that, with the progress of planning, the domestic supply of investment goods would become more and more important. That is, although in the beginning India will, no doubt, have to depend on imports of capital goods, the policy would be to make India *independent* of such imports as soon as possible.[2] In the present model I have, therefore, assumed that there would be no imports or exports of investment goods.

5. Let Y_t = national income, C_t = consumption, and K_t = investment at time t; with Y_0, C_0, K_0 as the corresponding values at the initial period. As already mentioned, λ_k and λ_c

---

[1] P. C. Mahalanobis: "Some observations on the process of growth of national income". *Sankhyā*, **12**(4), 1953.

[2] This does not mean that India would not purchase capital goods from other countries. India would make such purchases but India would also manufacture and export capital goods. Secondly, if for any reason (such as lack of foreign currency, shortage of supply or high prices in the world market, state of blockade or war, etc.) there is difficulty in securing essential investment goods from abroad, India should be able to manufacture such goods within the country.

(with $\lambda_k + \lambda_c = 1$) are fractions of investment allocated to industries producing capital goods (K-sector) and consumer goods (C-sector) respectively. We shall write β_k = ratio of increment of income to investment in industries producing investment goods; β_c = ratio of increment of income to investment in industries producing consumer goods; and define β as the ratio of increment of income generated to total net investment in the economy as a whole, with

$$\beta = \lambda_k \beta_k + \lambda_c \beta_o, \quad \text{necessarily.}$$

We also have
$$K_{t+1} - K_t = \lambda_k \beta_k K_t, \qquad \dots \ (4.1)$$

$$C_{t+1} - C_t = \lambda_c \beta_c K_t. \qquad \dots \ (4.2)$$

We then get
$$K_t = (1 + \lambda_k \beta_k)^t K_0, \qquad \dots \ (4.3)$$

$$Y_t = Y_0 \left[1 + \alpha_0 \frac{\lambda_k \beta_k + \lambda_c \beta_c}{\lambda_k \beta_k} \left\{ (1 + \lambda_k \beta_k)^t - 1. \right\} \right] \qquad \dots \ (4.4)$$

giving national income in terms of the initial income Y_0, the initial rate of investment α_0, and the allocation parameters λ_k and λ_c (which are at our choice), and the contingent coefficients β_k and β_c (which, however, are determined by the pattern of investment and conditions of production).

A FOUR-SECTOR MODEL

6. More recently I found it of great help to use a four-sector model. The two-sector model described above is first used to decide the allocation λ_k to the industries producing capital or investment goods. The industries producing consumer goods and services are divided into three different sectors, namely, factory production of consumer goods (sector $C.1$); the production of consumer goods (including agricultural products) in small and household industries (sector $C.2$); and services such as health, education etc., (sector $C.3$).

7. As creating new employment is an important aim of planning in India, we introduce another set of parameters, θ's, the net investment required per engaged person. The number of jobs created in any sector, which we may call n, is then simply λ / θ per unit investment where λ is the fraction of investment allocated to

the sector under consideration. We shall use the subscript k for industries producing investment goods (K-sector); subscripts 1, 2, and 3 respectively for the industries producing consumer goods and services in the three sectors $C.1$, $C.2$ and $C.3$ respectively. We shall then have λ_k, λ_1, λ_2 and λ_3 as fractions of investment allocated to the K-sector, sector $C.1$, sector $C.2$ and sector $C.3$ respectively; with, of course,

$$\lambda_k + \lambda_1 + \lambda_2 + \lambda_3 = 1. \qquad \qquad \dots \ (4.5)$$

We also have β_k, β_1, β_2 and β_3 as the ratio of increment of income to investment; and θ_k, θ_1, θ_2 and θ_3 as the net investment required per engaged person respectively in the four sectors. We now consider a total plan-period of, say, 5 years, and regard the above parameters as average values appropriate to the plan-period as a whole. Also, if n_k, n_1, n_2 and n_3 are the number of additional persons engaged respectively in the four sectors over the plan-period, and A is the total investment over the whole plan-period, then

$$n_k = \lambda_k A / \theta_k, \ n_1 = \lambda_1 A / \theta_1, \ n_2 = \lambda_2 A / \theta_2, \text{ and } n_3 = \lambda_3 A / \theta_3. \ \dots \ (4.6)$$

If N is the total number of additional persons engaged over the plan-period, and E is the total increase in income over the whole plan-period, then we have

$$N = n_k + n_1 + n_2 + n_3, \qquad \qquad \dots \ (4.7)$$

$$A = n_k \theta_k + n_1 \theta_1 + n_2 \theta_2 + n_3 \theta_3$$

$$= \lambda_k A + n_1 \theta_1 + n_2 \theta_2 + n_3 \theta_3, \text{ since } n_k \theta_k = \lambda_k A \text{ from (4.6)} \ \dots \ (4.8)$$

Also, $\quad E = \beta_k \theta_k n_k + \beta_1 \theta_1 n_1 + \beta_2 \theta_2 n_2 + \beta_3 \theta_3 n_3$

$$\equiv Y_0 [(1+\eta)^5 - 1], \text{ say.} \qquad \qquad \dots \ (4.9)$$

If we assume a constant annual rate of growth of income of, say, η per cent per year, then E can be derived from the initial income per year Y_0 by applying the η rate to Y_0. For our calculations we have taken η as given and equal to 5 per cent per year.

8. In order to use the above model we must substitute statistical estimates for the different algebraic symbols in the equations. It

is possible to treat as 'variables' the increase in national income E, the investment A, and the employment N. But the ratio of net income generated to capital investment $\beta_k, \beta_1, \beta_2$ and β_3, and the net investment required per engaged person $\theta_k, \theta_1, \theta_2, \theta_3$ respectively for each of the four sectors behave as parameters; and are given in the sense that their respective values are assumed to remain more or less constant and are not sought to be influenced by planning during the period under consideration. Besides these, we have the allocation ratios $\lambda_k, \lambda_1, \lambda_2, \lambda_3$ which also are parametric in the sense that they do not change during the period of time under consideration. There is however an important distinction. The income-investment ratios β's are determined by the conditions of production (and the pattern of investments within each of the four sectors) and are not influenced by planning,[1] during the period under consideration. The allocation ratios λ's, on the other hand, are at the choice of the planner within certain limits. The proportion of total investment allocated to investment goods industries λ_k must be decided from considerations of long period changes; and the allocation ratios for the other sectors $\lambda_1, \lambda_2, \lambda_3$ must then be obtained as solutions of the set of simultaneous equations given above. For example, the rate of increase of income or the employment generated may be treated as 'variables' to which desired values may be assigned. The model would then enable us, with the help of numerical estimates of the various parameters, to study how the allocation ratios λ's, that is, the proportions of total investment going into the different sectors should be chosen so that the desired aims can be realized.

CONCEPTS AND DEFINITIONS

9. We have been using so far terms like 'national income', 'investment' etc., without giving any definitions. In order to make valid statistical estimates of the magnitudes of the different variables or parameters it is necessary to have operational definitions which can be used for statistical purposes in practice without ambiguity. There are different concepts of *national income*. We have used here the definition adopted in the United Nations publication 'A System of National Accounts and Supporting Tables' [23].[2] It

---

[1] The pattern of investment itself is, of course, determined by the programme of investments which results from planning. In this sense, the β-coefficients are also indirectly amenable to planning but only in an implicit or indirect way. In contrast, the λ-coefficients are subject to direct planning.

[2] Figures in square brackets indicate serial number of references on p. 84.

is possible to use other concepts, for example, the USSR definition of national income as the total net material product. Another possibility is to define national income as the sum of the net material product and the value of the directly consumed services; this concept may be particularly useful under planning in a country with a mixed economy like India. What is needed is a concept which would be most suitable for the purpose in view. Some tentative work has been started but no definite conclusions have been yet reached. In this situation I shall use United Nations definition which has wide acceptance. The latest available estimates of domestic product of India (according to UN definition) is for 1953-54 which has been used in our calculations [2]. Provisional estimates for 1954-55 and 1955-56 have been also prepared for our work by the Central Statistical Organization.

10. *Investment* is the net addition to capital stock within the country in the form of plant, machinery, buildings and other capital goods. There are considerable conceptual and estimational difficulties in calculating the net investment. Standards also vary from one country to another in the proportion of maintenance and repair expenses charged to the operating account. In highly industrialized countries like the USA, the UK, Sweden and Switzerland, during the last decade or two, the rate of investment appears to have been between 10 per cent and 13 per cent of the national product. In the UK, during the period 1870-1913, the average rate of net investment was about 11 per cent per year. In the USA the average rate was 12 per cent or 13 per cent over several decades and exceeded 16 per cent over a decennial period only on two occasions during 1879-1948. In Sweden the rate was about 11 per cent over a long period before the war and about 13 per cent after the war; and in Switzerland it was of the order of 10 or 11 per cent in recent years. In socialized countries the rate of net investment is higher and is roughly of the order of 15 or 16 per cent or 20 per cent or even more as seen from the available information about Poland, Czechoslovakia, Hungary, East Germany and USSR. The current rate of investment in India is estimated as being of the order of 7 per cent of the net national product. For rapid industrial development the rate of investment must be increased appreciably.* We have suggested that it should be

---

* Simon Kuznets (1952) has shown that the rate of savings out of disposable personal income was remarkably steady and did not rise with the increase of national income in the USA over a long period (1869–1938). This is likely to be

increased from about 7 per cent to about 10 or 11 per cent by the end of the Second Five Year Plan or should be about 9 per cent on an average during the plan-period.

11. *Employment*, as considered in the present model, is the equivalent number of new jobs that would be created as a result of planned investment and production. In a country like India there are a very large number of persons working on their own account. They do not hold paid posts, and cannot lose their jobs. Many of them, however, do not have enough work and remain idle a part of the time. In their case if the volume of gainful work increases it may not lead to the creation of new jobs but usually some additional members of the household (who used to be partly or wholly idle) would be absorbed (partly or wholly) in the household enterprises. The concept of employment in the present context is, therefore, much wider than that used in the highly industrialized countries. We shall include under employment the increase in the gainful work in the household sector and also part time employment so that the total new employment would represent the increase in terms of something like equivalent man-years.

Allocation to Capital Goods Industries

12. I shall now consider the proportion of investment that should be allocated to industries producing investment goods (λ_k) through planning. We found from available data that β_k is usually much smaller than β_c (that is, the marginal increase of income per unit of investment is much less in basic industries producing capital goods than in industries producing consumer goods). This being so, the larger the value of λ_k, the smaller is the increase of income in the short run; but, after a critical period of several years, income begins to rise very steeply. Using the initial rate of investment, $\alpha_0 = 7$ per cent, $\beta_k = 0.2$ and different plausible values of β_c we found that to attain a fairly rapid increase of income over, say, about 30 years, it would be desirable that λ_k should have a value between 0.3 and 0.5. We adopted the value $\lambda_k = 1/3$, as we felt

---

true in India also. Investments apparently can be increased in India in any appreciable manner either (a) by ploughing back undistributed profits in private enterprises or (b) through Government planning. To encourage large-scale ploughing back of undistributed profits (which would be practicable only in the case of the big private enterprises) would lead to progressive concentration of capital and financial power. This would be inconsistent with a socialistic pattern of economy. In India investments must be increased in the public sector through national planning.

it would not be possible to go beyond this value under present conditions. (See Technical Note at the end of this chapter.)

STATISTICAL ESTIMATES OF THE PARAMETERS

13. The next step is to obtain reasonable estimates of the parameters which occur in the model under study. In principle, it is possible to use time-series data provided prices and the pattern of production had remained fairly steady, and also provided production was up to full capacity. This method, however, cannot be used in India for lack of suitable time-series data. We shall have to rely a great deal, therefore, on short period or technological data.[1]

CURRENT OR REPLACEMENT VALUE OF CAPITAL

14. Investment is a basic item in the present model. It is desirable to express the value of investment at current (rather than historic) prices. For this purpose it is necessary to know the relation between the book value and the replacement value of capital. Consider a steady state in which the stock of capital goods is being maintained without any increase or decrease. Every type of capital goods has a certain life after which it must be replaced. Consider any particular type of capital goods, and let its average life be T years. Also consider any particular item of the given type; it must already have been in use for a certain period, say, t years; it then has $(T-t)$ years of useful life still left. If the stock of capital goods includes a large number of items of the given type then there would be one item which still has a useful life of t years left. We may pair these two items (of the same given type), one with useful life of $(T-t)$ years still left and the other with a balance of useful life of t years; then the combined useful life of the two items taken together is $(T-t)+t$ or equal to T years for two items. The average life is thus $\frac{1}{2}(T)$ for each item. This argument would be valid for all items (under the simplifying conditions mentioned above). Hence, the average useful life still left at any time is half of the total life, so that as a first approximation, the current book-value should be half of the replacement value. The replacement value of capital can be, therefore, taken as double the book value.[2]

---

[1] Estimates of β based on data for annual increment of income and investment are not strictly appropriate. I have not entered into refinements because subsequent calculations are of a very rough nature. (It is worth noting, however, that β-coefficients appear to be fairly stable over long periods.)

[2] This question has been discussed in detail under more general conditions by D. G. Champernowne and R. F. Kahn in *Review of Economic Studies*, vol. XXI (2), 1953-54.

A rough check was made in the following way. If we assume that
the paid-up capital is numerically equivalent to net block assets,
and inflate the annual increase in the paid-up capital by an index
of cost of capital construction (compiled from an index of construction cost and an index of import prices of machinery) for the last
few years, for India, then on aggregation the estimate of replacement value is actually found to be about double the present value
of the total paid-up capital (which is assumed to be the same as
the present book value of net block capital).

15. In a recent survey of 8 small-scale industries in the Calcutta area (1952-53) the replacement value of plant and machinery
was found to vary from 2 to 6 times the book value. Also, data on
the relation between the output and investment are available for
a number of projects. If these relations are used to estimate (on
the basis of current output) the capital stock in existing enterprises,
it is found in most cases that the estimates of replacement value
are 2 to 4 times the corresponding book values of capital. It is
necessary to remember that in these cases much of the plant
and machinery was purchased many years ago when prices were
very low compared to current prices. In addition to adjustments
for depreciation, it is, therefore, also necessary to make reasonable allowances for changes in the level of prices. These adjustments are particularly important in the case of plant and machinery but are not necessary in the case of stocks which are usually
valued roughly at current prices. Depreciation in the case of buildings would be comparatively small, but adjustments for cost of
construction would be necessary. On the basis of studies on the
lines explained above it was decided generally to use double the book
value as a reasonable estimate of the current replacement value.

Income-Coefficient of Capital (β)

16. One most useful parameter is the general (over-all average)
ratio of increment in income to investment defined by

$$\beta = \lambda_k \beta_k + \lambda_1 \beta_1 + \lambda_2 \beta_2 + \lambda_3 \beta_3. \qquad \ldots \quad (4.10)$$

I may first consider briefly the value of this parameter in foreign
countries. In the USA, during the period 1861-1938, the average
income coefficient of investment (β) was of the order of 30 per cent.
In the UK on the basis of data given by A. R. Prest (1948) and
by J. H. Lenfant (1951) over the period 1870-1913, I found by direct

APPROACH OF OPERATIONAL RESEARCH

calculation that it was about 25 per cent. However, much larger values of β are obtained over short periods. Thus, if all available statistics on increment of income and net investment recently released in various United Nations publications are utilised, we get an average estimate of the ratio of the order of 40 per cent for 19 countries. For Japan over the periods 1930-36 and 1947-52, the ratio is as high as 50 per cent. In the latest 'Economic Survey of Asia and the Far East for 1954' by ECAFE [25], the value of this ratio for a number of countries in South-East Asia is quoted (on page xiii) as varying between 40 per cent and 50 per cent.

17. I should also note in the present connexion that in a capitalistic country, when the study covers a fairly long period of time, usually there would be periods of both rising and falling national income. The income coefficient of investment (β) over the whole period would be an average of values of the coefficient during periods of both booms and depressions. The observed ratio would be high when income and investment are both increasing. On the other hand, whenever a part of the capital remains idle (during periods of depression) the observed value of β must necessarily fall.[1] This is fully corroborated, for example, for the USA, for the period 1929-52; the general average is of the order of 0.28 while the average of the positive values only is as high as 0.76 [10].

18. Under planning, the aim is to maintain a continually expanding economy with production at full capacity. In a socialized economy, production is deliberately planned to make the fullest use of all resources and by-products.[2] That is, attempt is made to attain the maximum external economies through planning with the result that values of β are large. In socialized countries the addition to the national product per unit of net new investment appears to be generally much higher than in private enterprise economy and is of the order of 0.6 or 0.7 or even higher.[3]

---

[1] If the trade cycle in capitalist economies is considered as a sum of harmonic fluctuations, then the average value (calculated with reference to the trend line) would be about half of the value of β taken over periods of production *above* the trend-line. If production to full or nearly full capacity can be maintained through planning then the value of β would seem to be doubled to a first approximation. That is, the capital coefficient would be roughly halved under planning.

[2] In a highly industrialized country like the USA, external economies become progressively more important and there is greater utilization of all by-products with the consequence that, during periods of increasing production, the value of β would tend to increase and approximate to the value attained in a planned economy. This may be at least a partial explanation of the observed increase in the value of β in the USA, in recent years.

[3] In discussions with Soviet economists I gathered the impression that the value of β can be as high as one hundred per cent or even more in certain

19. In India, for the First Five Year Plan, this β-coefficient was assumed to be of the order of 0.33 but the actual growth of income seems to have been higher than that envisaged in the plan. Over the six year period 1948-49 to 1953-54, the ratio of increment of income to investment was only slightly lower than 0.5 as revealed by the recent national income statistics.   Under conditions of planning the overall income coefficient of investment β in India may therefore be taken to be of the order of 0.5.

SECTORAL VALUES OF INCOME-COEFFICIENTS

20.   We may now consider the sectoral ratios β_k, β_1, β_2, β_3 bearing in mind that the overall ratio for the economy should be of the order of 0.5.   In the sector of capital goods industry, the observed average value of the income-coefficient, based on the Sample Survey of Manufacturing Industries (SSMI) relating to five successive years 1949-1953, comes out as 0.43, which when adjusted for replacement value gives a value of $\beta_k = 0.21$.

21.   The Census of Manufactures [3] gives an overall average of $\beta = 0.6$ for the five years 1946 to 1950.   This includes some investment goods industries, excluding which the income-coefficient for factory production of consumer goods would be somewhat higher and of the order of 0.7. This figure, however, refers to the book value of capital; adjusting by the factor of $\frac{1}{2}$ for replacement value, we get a corresponding income-coefficient for replacement value of $\beta_1 = 0.35$.

22.   For agriculture, very little direct data are available for estimation of the parameter.   We have to use, therefore, the national income data on income and investment which yield a figure of about 1.5 for both agriculture and household enterprises combined.   There was, however, a large and somewhat sudden increase in agricultural production which has pushed up the national income figures since 1951-52; a part of this increase is usually ascribed to exceptionally good monsoons, and a part may be due to a statistical correction of previous under-estimation in official figures of crop production. We have thought it advisable to scale down the figure slightly and have adopted $\beta_2 = 1.25$ as a reasonable value.

23.   Some fragmentary data are available on the income-coefficient in the small and household industries which we may call

---

transitional phases of planned economy, that is, the new net income generated may be equal to or even higher than the new investment which is associated with this income.

β_h. The National Sample Survey, fourth round (April-September, 1952) gave a value of $\beta_h = 2.1$. From an earlier survey at Aligarh-Harduaganj in 1948, the income-coefficient was found to be about 2 in rural areas and 1.7 in urban areas. The material supplied by the All-India Khadi and Village Industries Board leads to a value of 2.8. A Survey of Small Scale Industries in Calcutta in 1952-53* had given a much smaller value of 0.94. It had been, however, noted in the report that the small enterprises were passing through a depression and that there was much idle capacity. The value at full capacity would be, therefore, much higher. On the basis of the above material, we have adopted a value of $\beta_h = 2$ (for use in paragraph 28, below).

24. The estimate of income-coefficient of investment for services was obtained as a straight average of figures obtained from balance sheet data released by the Reserve Bank of India [20]. It was found that $\beta_3 = 0.45$ approximately.

NUMERICAL VALUES OF CAPITAL REQUIRED PER ENGAGED PERSON (θ)

25. We must next consider estimates of θ, the capital needed per employed person in the individual sectors under study. In the industries producing investment goods (K-sector) the average capital needed per person in the five successive rounds of SSMI (1949-1953) was about Rs. 6,200 only while the figure relating to 1953 alone was about Rs. 8,500 (both figures at book value). Adjusting for replacement value, the average value of θ_k would come to something between Rs. 12,000 and Rs. 17,000 per engaged person.

26. It must be remembered, however, that India is greatly lacking in the basic heavy industries (metals, machinery, heavy chemicals, etc.), on which emphasis will have to be given in the near future. We therefore, made some calculations on the basis of new projects which are being prepared for the Second Five Year Plan. We find that the capital needed per worker ranges from Rs. 35,000 to Rs. 60,000 for industries like iron and steel or machine tools while it is about Rs. 12,000 or somewhat less for industries like cement, aluminium, coal and electricity. The appropriate average for the sector has to be chosen in accordance with the pattern of development of the capital goods industry in the Second Plan. As our intention is to expand rapidly the basic heavy investment

---

* Bureau of Industrial Statistics, Calcutta, 1953.

goods industries, we have adopted Rs. 20,000 per person as a reasonable figure for the capital coefficient of employment θ_k in this sector.

27. Large scale industries for the production of consumer goods which are included in the Programmes of Industrial Development published by the Planning Commission [7] yield an average value of θ_1 of about Rs. 10,000 per person. The adjusted figure from the Census of Manufactures for the year 1950 is Rs. 7,528. We have adopted Rs. 8,750 as a reasonable estimate of the capital needed per engaged person in the large scale factory production of consumer goods.

28. For small scale and household industries the following material is available on the capital requirement per person, θ_2. The National Sample Survey, third round and fourth round figures are Rs. 430 and Rs. 360 respectively. A survey of small scale industries at Aligarh-Harduaganj, conducted by the Ministry of Industry in 1948, gave Rs. 114 for rural areas and Rs. 465 for urban areas. These figures all refer to what are usually called cottage or household industries of a traditional type. According to the Survey of Small Scale Industries of Calcutta in 1952-53[9], which covered mostly the production of components for large engineering enterprises, the amount of capital needed per worker was much higher and about Rs. 1,200 per person. The unweighted average of the above estimates is Rs. 620. For agriculture, some data on the cultivation of reclaimed lands and of lands brought under major irrigation schemes give the capital per person as about Rs. 6,250. Using approximate weights for the small scale industries and agriculture, we got Rs. 2,500 per engaged person as a reasonable estimate for the sector of agriculture and small scale and household industries combined (θ_2).

29. For the services sector, the capital coefficient of employment (θ_3) was calculated on the basis of outlay and employment in education and health schemes, transport services, etc., yielding a figure of about Rs. 3,750.

A NUMERICAL SOLUTION OF THE FOUR-SECTOR MODEL

30. We can now get a solution for our four-sector model. On the basis of an average rate of investment of 9 per cent (as indicated in paragraph 10 above) and from considerations of financial resources we adopted, in consultation with the Economic Divisions of the Planning Commission and of the Ministry of Finance, Rs. 5,600 crores as the target of total asset formation during the plan-period

of 5 years.   We accept $\eta = 5$ per cent as the assigned rate of increase
of national income per year; and $N = 110$ lakhs or 11 million as
the number of jobs to be created during the plan period of 5 years.
We thus start with :

$Y_0 =$ initial national income $= $ Rs. 10,800 crores.
$A = $ total asset formation $= $ Rs. 5,600 crores.
$\eta = $ rate of increase of national income $= 5$ per cent per year.
$N = $ total new employment to be created $= 110$ lakhs($= 11$ million).
$\lambda_k = $ proportion of investment in industries
        producing investment goods $= 0.33$ (settled from
                                      considerations of
                                      growth over a long
                                      period).

We can also write down the sectoral coefficient :

sector	description	parameters	
		β	θ
K	basic investment goods	$\beta_k = 0.20,$	$\theta_k = $ Rs. 20,000
$C.1$	factory consumer goods	$\beta_1 = 0.35,$	$\theta_1 = $ Rs. 8,750
$C.2$	household industries (including agriculture)	$\beta_2 = 1.25,$	$\theta_2 = $ Rs. 2,500
$C.3$	services	$\beta_3 = 0.45,$	$\theta_3 = $ Rs. 3,750

For a plan-period of 5 years, we then get the following results in
rounded figures :

sectors	investment (A) (Rs. crores)	increase in	
		income (E) (Rs. crores)	employment (N) (million)
K	1850	370	0.9
$C.1$	980	340	1.1
$C.2$	1180	1470	4.7
$C.3$	1600	720	4.3
	5610	2900	11.0

We have, therefore, obtained the allocation of the total investment
and the total man-power between the four broad sectors of the
economy.

31.   We shall next split up the estimates relating to the combined sector of agriculture and small and household industries into two sub-sectors: (1) agriculture, and (2) small and household enterprises. For this, we can use a subsidiary system of simultaneous equations similar to the one cited earlier.   Using the subscript a for the sector of agriculture and h for the sector of household enterprises we may write the employment created in the two sectors respectively as n_a and n_h and the corresponding parameters as β_a, θ_a and β_h, θ_h. Using the numerical values for the combined sector given in the previous paragraph, we then have the following equations

$n_a + n_h = n_2$ = combined employment = 4.7 million,

$n_a \theta_a + n_h \theta_h$ = combined investment = Rs. 1,180 crores,

$\beta_a n_a \theta_a + \beta_h n_h \theta_h$ = combined increase in income = Rs. 1,470 crores.

We can now substitute the value of β_h from paragraph 23, and of θ_a and θ_h from paragraph 28.

$$\beta_h = 2, \quad \theta_a = \text{Rs. } 6,250, \quad \text{and} \quad \theta_h = \text{Rs. } 620.$$

On solution, we get the ratio of increment of income to investment for agriculture β_a as 1.10; and the allocation of increase in income, employment generated, and investment as shown below.

	sector	investment (Rs. crores)	increment in income (Rs. crores)	increment in employment (million)
a	agriculture	986	1083	1.58
h	household enterprises	194	387	3.12
		1180	1470	4.70

Comparison with Figures Given in the Plan-frame

32.   In the Draft Plan-frame, we have retained the above broad sector allocations and have adjusted allocations within sectors to some extent from considerations which are explained later.   The figures given in the Draft Plan-frame are compared in the following table with the figures obtained from the numerical solution given above.   The allocation of investment and employment in the Planframe is found to be in line with the solution.

| sector | investment (Rs. crores) | | increment in | | | |
| | | | income (Rs. crores) | | employment (million) | |
	plan-frame	this paper	plan-frame	this paper	plan-frame	this paper
$K+C.1$	2800	2830	710	710	2.1	2.0
$C.2$	1150	1180	1470	1470	4.5	4.7
agriculture	950	986	1060	1083	1.5	1.6
household enterprises	200	194	410	387	3.0	3.1
$C.3$	1650	1600	720	720	4.4	4.3
total	5600	5610	2900	2900	11.0	11.0

33. I shall now consider certain definitional questions which arise in splitting up the figures of investment relating to the sector of large scale enterprises, that is, between sector K (industries producing investment goods) and the sector $C.1$ (factories producing consumer goods). It has been already pointed out that the intermediate products should be allocated to the two sectors in such a way as to obtain the net outputs of both the sectors as final products. Since by choice, 33 per cent of Rs. 5,600 crores, that is, Rs. 1,850 crores of the total investment is allocated to investment goods industries, it follows that the remaining Rs. 950 crores must go to large scale industries producing consumer goods ($C.1$). The two above amounts of investment in the two sectors (Rs. 1,850 crores and Rs. 950 crores respectively) should conceptually include the investments on intermediate goods which are used in respective sectors. Further, it is necessary to allocate the investment on stocks. For this, we have taken three-fifths of the stocks as trading stocks (Rs. 300 crores) and the rest (Rs. 200 crores) as inventories of large scale industries. Thus, the investment pattern presented in the Plan-frame now works out as follows.

sector		industry	investment (Rs. crores)
K		basic investment goods	1850
$C.1$		factory consumer goods	950
$C.2 = (a)+(h)$		household industries	1150
	(a)	agriculture	950
	(h)	household enterprises	200
$C.3$		services	1650
			5600

34.   In the next table the above figures are reconciled with the investment figures actually given in Chapter Three, Table (2) of the Draft Plan-frame.* The allocation of investments was shown there as Rs. 500 crores for electricity (including hydro-electric projects combined with irrigation schemes); Rs. 1,400 crores for large scale industries; and Rs. 900 crores for transport (railways, roads etc). The total of these three heads comes to Rs. 2,800 crores which may be identified with the total of Rs. 2,830 crores for the K-sector and the sector $C.1$ taken together (as shown in lines 1, 2 and 3 of the following Table). This total can be also broken down into an investment of Rs. 1,850 crores in industries producing investment goods (line 4) and an investment of Rs. 980 crores in this paper or Rs. 950 crores in the Plan-frame (line 5). Agriculture and irrigation (line 6) have been alloted Rs. 950 crores in the Plan-frame corresponding to Rs. 985 crores in this paper; and household enterprises Rs. 200 crores (line 7 of the following Table). The services sector with an allocation of investment of Rs. 1,600 crores has been treated as covering all construction work (buildings for schools, hospitals, residences, roads, etc.) and also trading stocks of Rs. 300 crores.

| sector | plan-frame | | | this paper (Rs. crores) |
	public	private (Rs. crores)	total	
1. electricity	450	50	500	
2. industry (large-scale)	1000	400	1400	
3. transport (railways, etc.)	850	50	900	
			2800	2830
4. of which investment goods			1850	1850
5. „ consumer goods			950	980
6. agriculture & irrigation	950	—	950	986
7. household enterprises	—	200	200	194
			1150	1180
8. construction, etc.	250	1100	1350	
9. stocks	—	300	300	
			1650	1600
10. grand total			5600	5610

* Out of total stocks of Rs. 500 crores given in Chapter Three, Table (2) of the Plan-frame, Rs. 200 crores have been transferred to industry (large scale) in the present table; at the same time Rs. 200 crores included under the head industry in the Plan-frame have been separated under household enterprises (Rs. 200 crores) in the present table.

35. This is as far as our simple model can take us. Further details must be settled from supplementary considerations. For example, the four-sector model cannot give any guidance to decide the share of investments in the public and the private sectors respectively. The allocation shown above is based partly on historical trends and partly on social policy. Large scale expansion of power plants (often in combination with irrigation schemes in river valley projects) in recent years has occurred mostly in the public sector and railways in India have been mainly State concerns for a long time. In the case of electricity and transport most of the investments would, therefore, take place in the public sector and has been shown in this way. On the other hand, there was very little of large scale industries in the public sector during the First Five Year Plan. The bigger share has been, however, reserved for the public sector in the Plan-frame because it is considered desirable to develop the basic industries (minerals, steel, heavy machines, heavy chemicals etc.) as quickly as possible which would be facilitated if such basic industries are State enterprises.

TECHNICAL NOTE ON THE PATTERN OF THE GROWTH OF THE ECONOMY
TWO-SECTOR MODEL

1. In the two-sector model the pattern of the growth of the economy depends on the initial rate of investment (which is given), the values of β_k and β_c, the income-coefficients respectively in the industries producing capital goods (K-sector) and in the industries producing consumer goods (C-sector) which are determined by technological factors and conditions of production and are not at the choice of the planner, and on λ_k, the fraction of the total investment allocated to industries producing capital goods (K-sector) with the remaining share of investments $\lambda_c(\equiv 1-\lambda_k)$ going to industries producing consumer goods.

2. The value $\lambda_k = 1/3$ was adopted on the basis of the pattern of growth emerging from certain values of β_k and β_c which were considered to be reasonable estimates of these parameters under Indian conditions. If the real values of β_k and β_c happen to be different from the values used in the model then the actual pattern of growth would be different from the pattern assumed to be true in the Plan-frame. The effect of a change in β_k or β_c can be studied numerically without any difficulty. I am giving four specimen tables to indicate the differences in the pattern of growth of the economy. Tables (A-1), (A-2) and (A-3) are appropriate to values of $\beta_k = 0.15$, 0.20, 0.25 respectively; and Table (A-4) gives some extreme values to illustrate boundary conditions.

3. It is seen from Tables (A-1) and (A-2) that for any value of β_c (with given β_k) the growth of the economy is slower for larger values of λ_k upto a *critical period*. Once the critical period is passed the higher the value of λ_k or β_k (or of both) the quicker is the growth of the income over a long period of 20 or 30 years.

4. It is not necessary to go into the details of the present tables but I may illustrate their use in one particular case. Columns (2) and (3) of Table (A-2) may be taken to represent what is likely to happen if the Indian economy continues without planning. Using $\beta_c = 0.25$, income will increase by about 42 per cent in 20 years. On the other hand, columns (7) and (8) may represent growth under planning. Firstly, the value of λ_k can be deliberately

TABLE (A-1): VALUES OF Y_t (= INCOME AT TIME t) FOR TWO-SECTOR MODEL

$Y_0 = 1,000$, $\alpha_0 = 7$ per cent, $\beta_k = 0.15$, $\beta_e = 0.25, 0.50, 0.75$ and 1.00 (for each value of $\lambda_k = 0.1, 0.3, 0.5, 0.7$)

year	$\lambda_k = 0.1$				$\lambda_k = 0.3$				$\lambda_k = 0.5$				$\lambda_k = 0.7$			
β_c	0.25	0.50	0.75	1.00	0.25	0.50	0.75	1.00	0.25	0.50	0.75	1.00	0.25	0.50	0.75	1.00
(1)	(2)	(3)	(4)	(5)	(6)	(7)	(8)	(9)	(10)	(11)	(12)	(13)	(14)	(15)	(16)	(17)
0	1000	1000	1000	1000	1000	1000	1000	1000	1000	1000	1000	1000	1000	1000	1000	1000
1	1017	1033	1048	1064	1015	1028	1040	1052	1014	1023	1032	1040	1013	1018	1023	1028
2	1034	1066	1097	1129	1031	1057	1082	1107	1029	1047	1065	1084	1027	1038	1049	1060
3	1051	1099	1147	1195	1048	1087	1125	1164	1045	1073	1102	1130	1042	1059	1077	1094
4	1069	1133	1198	1262	1066	1118	1171	1223	1063	1102	1141	1180	1059	1083	1108	1133
5	1087	1168	1249	1330	1084	1151	1218	1285	1081	1132	1183	1234	1078	1110	1142	1175
6	1105	1203	1301	1399	1103	1186	1268	1350	1101	1165	1228	1292	1098	1139	1180	1222
7	1123	1238	1354	1469	1123	1222	1320	1418	1123	1200	1277	1354	1121	1172	1223	1273
8	1142	1274	1407	1540	1144	1259	1374	1489	1146	1238	1329	1420	1147	1208	1269	1330
9	1161	1311	1462	1612	1166	1299	1431	1563	1171	1278	1385	1492	1175	1248	1320	1393
10	1180	1348	1517	1686	1189	1340	1490	1641	1198	1322	1446	1569	1206	1291	1377	1463
20	1388	1753	2117	2481	1483	1867	2252	2636	1606	1985	2364	2743	1764	2082	2401	2719
30	1630	2222	2813	3404	1939	2687	3434	4182	2448	3352	4257	5162	3399	4399	5398	6398

TABLE (A-2): VALUES OF Y_t (= INCOME AT TIME t) FOR TWO-SECTOR MODEL

$Y_o = 1,000$, $a_o = 7$ per cent, $\beta_k = 0.20$, $\beta_c = 0.25, 0.50, 0.75, 1.00$ (for each value of $\lambda_k = 0.1, 0.3, 0.5$ and 0.7)

	$\lambda_k = 0.1$				$\lambda_k = 0.3$				$\lambda_k = 0.5$				$\lambda_k = 0.7$			
β_c year	0.25	0.50	0.75	1.00	0.25	0.50	0.75	1.00	0.25	0.50	0.75	1.00	0.25	0.50	0.75	1.00
(1)	(2)	(3)	(4)	(5)	(6)	(7)	(8)	(9)	(10)	(11)	(12)	(13)	(14)	(15)	(16)	(17)
0	1000	1000	1000	1000	1000	1000	1000	1000	1000	1000	1000	1000	1000	1000	1000	1000
1	1017	1033	1049	1064	1016	1029	1041	1053	1016	1024	1033	1042	1015	1020	1026	1031
2	1035	1066	1098	1130	1034	1059	1084	1110	1033	1051	1070	1088	1032	1043	1055	1066
3	1052	1101	1149	1197	1052	1091	1130	1169	1052	1081	1110	1139	1052	1070	1088	1106
4	1071	1136	1201	1265	1072	1126	1179	1233	1073	1114	1154	1195	1074	1100	1126	1152
5	1089	1171	1253	1335	1093	1162	1231	1300	1096	1150	1203	1256	1099	1134	1169	1204
6	1108	1208	1307	1406	1115	1200	1286	1371	1122	1189	1257	1324	1128	1173	1218	1263
7	1127	1245	1362	1479	1138	1241	1344	1447	1149	1232	1315	1398	1161	1218	1274	1330
8	1147	1282	1418	1553	1163	1284	1405	1527	1180	1280	1380	1480	1199	1269	1338	1408
9	1167	1321	1475	1628	1189	1330	1471	1611	1214	1333	1452	1570	1242	1327	1411	1495
10	1188	1360	1533	1705	1217	1378	1540	1701	1251	1390	1530	1669	1291	1393	1494	1596
20	1417	1799	2182	2565	1605	2056	2506	2957	1902	2403	2904	3406	2370	2848	3326	3804
30	1696	2335	2974	3613	2301	3269	4237	5206	3591	5030	6469	7909	6370	8243	10116	11989

TABLE (A-3). VALUES OF Y_t (= INCOME AT TIME t) FOR TWO-SECTOR MODEL

$Y_0 = 1,000$ $\alpha_0 = 7$ per cent, $\beta_k = 0.25$ $\beta_c = 0.25,\ 0.50,\ 0.75,\ 1.00$ (for each value of $\lambda_k = 0.1,\ 0.3,\ 0.5$ and 0.7)

year	$\lambda_k = 0.1$				$\lambda_k = 0.3$				$\lambda_k = 0.5$				$\lambda_k = 0.7$			
β_c	0.25	0.50	0.75	1.00	0.25	0.50	0.75	1.00	0.25	0.50	0.75	1.00	0.25	0.50	0.75	1.00
(1)	(2)	(3)	(4)	(5)	(6)	(7)	(8)	(9)	(10)	(11)	(12)	(13)	(14)	(15)	(16)	(17)
0	1000	1000	1000	1000	1000	1000	1000	1000	1000	1000	1000	1000	1000	1000	1000	1000
1	1018	1033	1049	1065	1017	1030	1042	1054	1018	1026	1035	1044	1018	1023	1028	1033
2	1035	1067	1099	1131	1036	1062	1087	1113	1037	1056	1074	1093	1038	1049	1061	1072
3	1054	1102	1151	1199	1057	1096	1136	1175	1059	1089	1119	1148	1062	1081	1100	1118
4	1073	1138	1203	1269	1078	1133	1188	1243	1084	1126	1169	1211	1091	1118	1145	1172
5	1092	1175	1258	1340	1102	1173	1244	1315	1112	1168	1225	1281	1124	1161	1198	1236
6	1112	1212	1313	1414	1127	1216	1304	1393	1144	1216	1288	1360	1163	1212	1261	1310
7	1132	1251	1370	1489	1154	1261	1369	1477	1179	1269	1359	1448	1209	1272	1335	1398
8	1153	1290	1428	1566	1183	1311	1439	1567	1219	1329	1438	1548	1263	1342	1421	1500
9	1174	1331	1488	1645	1214	1364	1514	1663	1264	1396	1528	1660	1327	1425	1523	1621
10	1196	1373	1549	1725	1248	1421	1594	1767	1315	1472	1629	1787	1402	1522	1643	1763
20	1447	1849	2252	2654	1758	2288	2829	3349	2336	3004	3673	4341	3416	4141	4866	5591
30	1768	2460	3151	3843	2809	4076	5343	6609	5654	7981	10308	12635	13522	17279	21036	24792

TABLE (A-4) :   VALUE OF Y_t (= INCOME AT t) FOR TWO-SECTOR MODEL

$Y_o = 1,000$, $\alpha_o = 7$ per cent, $\beta_k = 0.1, 0.2, 0.4$, $\beta_c = 0.25, 0.75, 1.25$, $\lambda_k = 0.1, 0.3, 0.7$,

year (1)	β_c	$\lambda_k = 0.1$			$\lambda_k = 0.3$			$\lambda_k = 0.7$		
		0.25 (2)	0.75 (3)	1.25 (4)	0.25 (5)	0.75 (6)	1.25 (7)	0.25 (8)	0.75 (9)	1.25 (10)
$\beta_k = 0.1$	5	1084	1245	1405	1076	1206	1336	1058	1119	1179
	10	1172	1502	1831	1165	1445	1726	1140	1285	1430
	20	1362	2056	2749	1386	2044	2702	1416	1847	2277
	30	1572	2668	3764	1683	2848	4014	1959	2951	3942
	50	2060	4091	6122	2618	5382	8146	5126	9395	13663
$\beta_k = 0.2$	5	1089	1253	1417	1093	1231	1369	1099	1169	1238
	10	1188	1533	1878	1217	1540	1863	1291	1494	1697
	20	1417	2182	2947	1605	2506	3408	2370	3326	4281
	30	1696	2974	4252	2301	4237	6174	6370	10116	13862
	50	2451	5115	7779	5776	12889	20003	76168	128611	181053
$\beta_k = 0.4$	5	1100	1271	1442	1131	1287	1442	1216	1308	1399
	10	1223	1601	1979	1362	1792	2222	1959	2364	2769
	20	1552	2490	3428	2488	4253	6018	13281	18470	23660
	30	2040	3807	5574	5983	11896	17809	146949	208619	270289
	50	3832	8641	13450	50560	109361	168161	20355669	28956374	37557079

increased from 0.1 to 0.3. Secondly, the value of β_c is bound to be higher and may be safely taken as 0.5 in which case the income will easily double in 20 years. If β_c increases under planning to 0.75, income would increase two and a half times in 20 years.

5. Professor J. B. S. Haldane considered the question of maximization of national income in the above model in a paper received in March 1954 which was printed in *Sankhyā*, Vol. 16, Parts 1 & 2.

FOUR-SECTOR MODEL

6. In the Plan-frame it is estimated that the volume of new employment would be about 11 million consisting of about 2.1 million in the large-scale (capital-intensive) industries, 4.5 million in agriculture and small and household (capital-light) industries and 4.4 million in the services. These estimates are based on the following values of the income-coefficients of investment (β's) and the capital required per engaged person (θ's) for the different sectors.

sector of the economy		sectoral income-coefficient of investment (β)	sectoral value of capital per engaged person (θ)
symbol	description		
(1)	(2)	(3)	(4)
K	large-scale industries producing investment goods	0.20	Rs. 20,000
$C.1$	large-scale industries producing consumer goods	0.35	,, 8,750
$C.2$	agriculture and small and household industries	1.25	,, 2,500
$C.3$	services (health, education etc.)	0.45	,, 3,750

7. If the targets of employment are changed from those given in the Plan-frame then the estimates of investment and income would also have to be changed in an appropriate manner. However, the accuracy of all such calculations depends on the accuracy of the adopted values of β's and θ's. If the actual values of β's and θ's (which are contingent parameters determined by technological factors and conditions of production and cannot be settled at the choice of the planners) happen to be different from those used in the Plan-frame then the derived estimates of employment, investment, and income would all have to be changed in an appropriate way. It is possible to study the effect of using different sets of values of β's and θ's. Numerical solutions to the model

8

used in the Plan-frame have been obtained; and calculated values of employment, investment, and income are given in columns (5), (6) and (7) respectively of Table (A-5) (*vide* p. 60) based on the respective values of β's and θ's given in columns (3) and (4) of the same table.

8. Let us suppose that the values of all θ's are doubled but β's remain the same, and the total fund to be invested also remains the same, namely, Rs. 5,600 crores. From lines 1-5 of Table (A-5), it is seen that the rise in national income can be large, about 6 per cent per year if we are satisfied with a low target of employment of 6 million (with a very high figure of 4.3 million in agriculture and small and household industries and a very low one of about half a million in the services).

9. Keeping the β's the same, if the θ's are changed to Rs. 30,000, Rs. 13,125, Rs. 3,750 and Rs. 5,625 for the 4 sectors respectively (lines 6-10), it is still possible to have an increase of income of 6 per cent per year together with new employment of 8 million out of which 1.5 million would be in large scale factories, 5.8 million in agriculture and household production and 0.7 in services. With the above values of β's and θ's it is also possible to achieve 6 per cent rise in income per year and new employment of 9 million over 5 years with, however, only 0.67 million in large scale factories together with 5.4 million in agriculture and household enterprises, and 2.9 million in services (lines 11-15). Employment can be increased to 10 million only if θ's can be lowered to Rs. 26,600, Rs. 11,638, Rs. 3,325 and Rs. 4,988 as shown in lines 16-20 of Table (A-5).

10. Let us next consider a case in which β's have lower values, namely, 0.15, 0.25, 0.75, 0.30 respectively, and θ's have higher values, namely, Rs. 40,000, Rs. 20,000, Rs. 5,000 and Rs. 10,000 respectively (lines 21-25) but the total investment is the same, Rs. 5,600 crores as in the Plan-frame. This represents a more unfavourable situation than that assumed in the Plan-frame. It is possible to attain a rate of increase of income of 5 per cent per year with, however, a low target of employment of 7 million with heavy concentration of 5.7 million in agriculture and household industries, only 0.54 million in large scale factories, and 0.72 million in services. Using the same values of β's and θ's as above, the same total employment of 7 million can be reached with, however, a much better distribution (1.4 million in factories and 2 million in services) if the increase in income can be lowered to about 4 per cent per year

(lines 26-30). Using the same values of β's but with another set of values of θ's (lines 31-35) it is still possible to have new employment of 7 million.

11. In more favourable cases with higher values of β's and lower values of θ's (lines 36-40) it is possible to have an increase of income of about 6 per cent per year with new employment of 13 million out of which 2.3 million would be in large scale factories. If the total employment is reduced to 12 million then a much larger number, 3 million, can be absorbed in factory industries (lines 41-45). With somewhat higher values of β's but the same values of θ's and the same investment of Rs. 5,600 (lines 46-50) it is possible to attain a 6 per cent increase in income per year and new employment of 12 million out of which 2.6 million would be in large factories.

12. If the income and investment figures are the same as in the Plan-frame and β's also have the same values but 20 per cent *less* employment needs to be created then it is possible to work with higher values of θ's (lines 51-55). On the other hand, in the same situation, if 20 per cent *more* employment has to be created, then the values of θ's must be much lower than those assumed in the Plan-frame (lines 56-60).

13. If β's and θ's retain the same values as in the Plan-frame but 20 per cent *less* employment has to be created then a much lower investment of Rs. 4,500 would be sufficient with, however, a smaller rate of rise of income of 4 per cent per year (lines 61-65). If in the same situation 20 per cent *more* men require to be employed then the investment would have to be increased to Rs. 6,700 crores with an increase of income at the rate of a little over 6 per cent per year (lines 66-70). It is possible in the same way to work out appropriate numerical solutions to study the effect of other values of the parameters or of the variables.

Change in the Value of β-Coefficients

14. It has been already pointed out (Chapter 4, para 18, p. 43) that the average value of β is likely to be appreciably higher in a planned economy as production would continue, in principle, at full capacity. One aim of planning would be to chose λ_i's in such a way as to make β as large as possible over a long period. Although the λ_i's are not independent, (being connected through inter-industry relations), some improvement in the overall pattern of production would be usually possible by an optimum utilization of resources at the given level of investment. For example,

TABLE (A-5) : EXPECTED VALUES OF EMPLOYMENT AND INCOME : FOUR–SECTOR MODEL

serial no.	sector of economy (i)	sectoral income coefficient (β_i)	capital per engaged person (in Rs.) (θ_i)	employ-ment (in million)	invest-ment (in Rs. crores)	income (in Rs. crores)	remarks
(1)	(2)	(3)	(4)	(5)	(6)	(7)	(8)
1	K	0.20	40,000	0.46	1,848	370	
2	$C.1$	0.35	17,500	0.68	1,193	418	34 p.c. increase in
3	$C.2$	1.25	5,000	4.34	2,167	2,708	income
4	$C.3$	0.45	7,500	0.52	392	176	
5	total	....	....	6.00	5,600	3,672	
6	K	0.20	30,000	0.62	1,848	370	
7	$C.1$	0.35	13,125	0.91	1,193	418	34 p.c. increase in
8	$C.2$	1.25	3,750	5.77	2,167	2,708	income
9	$C.3$	0.45	5,625	0.70	392	176	
10	total	....	....	8.00	5,600	3,672	
11	K	0.20	30,000	0.62	1,848	370	
12	$C.1$	0.35	13,125	0.07	88	31	34 p.c. increase in
13	$C.2$	1.25	3,750	5.40	2,028	2,535	income
14	$C.3$	0.45	5,625	2.91	1,636	736	
15	total	....	....	9.00	5,600	3,672	
16	K	0.20	26,600	0.69	1,848	370	
17	$C.1$	0.35	11,638	0.20	235	82	34 p.c. increase in
18	$C.2$	1.25	3,325	6.16	2,047	2,558	income
19	$C.3$	0.45	4,988	2.95	1,470	662	
20	total	....	....	10.00	5,600	3,672	
21	K	0.15	40,000	0.46	1,848	277	
22	$C.1$	0.25	20,000	0.12	249	62	25 p.c. increase in
23	$C.2$	0.75	5,000	5.83	2,910	2,183	income
24	$C.3$	0.30	10,000	0.59	593	178	
25	total	...	...	7.00	5,600	2,700	
26	K	0.15	40,000	0.46	1,848	277	
27	$C.1$	0.25	10,000	0.97	966	242	20 p.c. increase in
28	$C.2$	0.75	5,000	3.58	1,790	1,342	income
29	$C.3$	0.30	5,000	1.99	996	299	
30	total	...	...	7.00	5,600	2,160	
31	K	0.15	30,000	0.62	1,848	277	
32	$C.1$	0.25	10,000	0.19	192	48	20 p.c. increase in
33	$C.2$	0.75	5,000	4.33	2,168	1,626	income
34	$C.3$	0.15	7,500	1.86	1,392	209	
35	total	...	...	7.00	5,600	2,160	

TABLE (A-5) EXPECTED VALUES OF EMPLOYMENT AND INCOME : FOUR-SECTOR MODEL (contd.)

serial no.	sector of economy (i)	sector income coefficient (β_i)	capital per engaged person (in Rs.) (θ_i)	employment (in million)	investment (in Rs. crores)	income (in Rs. crores)	remarks.
(1)	(2)	(3)	(4)	(5)	(6)	(7)	(8)
36	K	0.25	20,000	0.92	1,848	462	
37	C.1	0.40	7,500	1.41	1,055	422	30 p.c. increase in
38	C.2	1.50	2,000	5.04	1,008	1,511	income
39	C.3	0.50	3,000	5.63	1,689	845	
40	total	...	...	13.00	5,600	3,240	
41	K	0.20	20,000	0.92	1,848	370	
42	C.1	0.35	7,500	2.06	1,545	541	25 p.c. increase in
43	C.2	1.25	2,000	4.98	996	1,244	income
44	C.3	0.45	3,000	4.04	1,211	545	
45	total	...	...	12.00	5,600	2,700	
46	K	0.25	20,000	0.92	1,848	462	
47	C.1	0.40	7,500	1.72	1,288	515	30 p.c. increase in
48	C.2	2.00	2,000	3.44	687	1,375	income
49	C.3	0.50	3,000	5.92	1,777	888	
50	total	...	...	12.00	5,600	3,240	
51	K	0.20	25,000	0.74	1,848	370	investment and in-
52	C.1	0.35	11,000	0.85	935	327	come as in plan-
53	C.2	1.25	3,125	3.74	1,169	1,462	frame; 20 p.c. less
54	C.3	0.45	4,750	3.47	1,648	741	employment.
55	total	...	...	8.80	5,600	2,900	
56	K	0.20	16,667	1.11	1,848	370	investment and in-
57	C.1	0.35	7,300	1.31	955	334	come as in plan-
58	C.2	1.25	2,090	5.60	1,172	1,465	frame; 20 p.c. more
59	C.3	0.45	3,140	5.18	1,625	731	employment.
60	total	...	...	13.20	5,600	2,900	
61	K	0.20	20,000	0.74	1,479	296	β's and θ's as in plan-
62	C.1	0.35	8,750	0.90	785	275	frame; 20 p.c. less
63	C.2	1.25	2,500	3.76	940	1,175	employment, invest-
64	C.3	0.45	3,750	3.40	1,276	574	ment and income.
65	total	...	.	8.80	4,480	2,320	
66	K	0.20	20,000	1.11	2,218	444	β's and θ's as in
67	C.1	0.35	8,750	1.35	1,178	412	plan-frame; 20 p.c.
68	C.2	1.25	2,500	5.64	1,411	1,763	more of employment,
69	C.3	0.45	3,750	5.10	1,913	861	investment and in-
70	total			13.20	6,720	3,480	come.

appreciable savings in transport may accrue through a properly planned location of units of production.

15.   The value of β would also depend on the rate of investment and on the stock of capital already accumulated. With a low rate of investment and a small stock of capital it would not be possible to utilize the resources in a complementary way to the fullest extent owing to indivisibilities in the scale of production.   The higher the rate of investment and the greater the stock of available capital the greater is the possibility of making the fullest use of the resources mobilized in the plan.   As already pointed out (Chapter 4, footnote 2, p. 43) in a country (like U S A) with a very high stock of capital it may become progressively easier to secure external economies and hence to have higher values of β. In India an important object of planning must be to increase the rate of investment and to build up quickly a large stock of capital which may, in its turn, lead to an increase in the value of β.   Technological improvements in methods of production would also increase the value of β.   When any technological improvement occurs either in a research institution or in a particular enterprise it would be possible to introduce the improved method quickly on an extensive scale in a planned economy.   At any given rate of investment and with a given stock of capital, for reasons explained above, the value of β is likely to be higher under planning.

16.   The value of the β-coefficients may, therefore, be expected to rise in India with the progress of planning in future. With any given amount of total assets formation (for example, Rs. 5,600 crores) and with any given set of values of the β-coefficients (for example, those used in this paper) there would be, in principle, an optimum allocation of resources in relation to the basic objectives (such as an increase of employment of 11 million and a long range rate of increase of income of 5 per cent per year).   If the values of the β-coefficients turn out in practice to be somewhat different then the solution used in the plan would not be a true optimum but may still serve as quite an efficient solution.   The illustrative tables given above show that the broad type of allocation used in the Draft Plan-frame is likely to be fairly efficient.   That is, the general approach of the Plan-frame is likely to be suitable for the purpose in view, and would have a good deal of scope for adjustments in details.

CHAPTER 5

SUPPLEMENTARY CONSIDERATIONS

1. The estimates of production, employment, income, and investment are given in the Draft Plan-frame by much finer categories than we have considered so far. Certain supplementary considerations have been used to derive these figures (which cannot be obtained from my theoretical model but are consistent with it). One basic step was to calculate the increase in demand of important consumer goods (cereals, cloth, sugar, etc.), which would be generated as a result of the (assigned) increase of 27 per cent in the national income in 5 years. This was done with the help of appropriate Engel elasticities* calculated on the basis of the National Sample Survey data. With the knowledge of the figures obtained from the solution described above, the targets of production were then fixed for the investment goods on partly *a priori* grounds, and for consumer goods on considerations of the anticipated additional demand. For some services, like transport, the targets were derived on the basis of targets of other sectors.

2. On the basis of this trial set of targets, the required investment and the employment generated were computed for individual targets by making use of appropriate technological coefficients. Also, the national income in 1952-53 was carried forward to 1955-56 and 1960-61 by making use of the physical production targets (the income arising from individual targets having been computed separately). For certain major commodities like cement, steel, coal, electricity, and heavy chemicals, the consistency of the trial set was then checked; for example, it was examined whether the production target for cement was equal to the demand for cement implicit in the levels of other targets. Then the trial targets were aggregated by sectors; and the calculated values of employment, income, and investment were checked against the solution. Naturally, a number of discrepancies were found in the beginning which necessitated changes in the targets. But gradually, by the method of repeated trial and error, a set of targets was obtained which was

---

* Some tentative values of Engel elasticities have been given in a Working Paper No. 8 of the Institute series on Plannng which was circulated in a mimeographed form in December 1954 and is now in the press.

consistent with the solution. Speaking broadly, this set of targets has been reproduced in the Plan-frame. Also, the figures of national income, employment, and investment as given in the Plan-frame were computed on the basis of the given set of targets in the manner described earlier.

3. To get the initial set of trial targets, a good deal of consideration was given to the physical resources and scarcities, existing economic conditions, and the opinion of various authorities on the desirable or possible increase of production during the plan period. For example, I have already mentioned that to instal a million ton steel plant at a cost of about Rs. 100 crores (Rs. 1000 million) it is necessary to import at present machinery to the value of about Rs. 45 or Rs. 50 crores. I have proposed in the Plan-frame that high priority should be given to establishing a heavy machine building industry to fabricate machinery required to produce steel and other investment goods. Once the heavy machine building industry is established it would be possible to increase investments progressively without depending on imports. Again, the supply of copper is short but India has large reserves of bauxite. It is logical to increase the production of aluminium to a sufficient extent to enable copper being replaced by aluminium in the electricity industry. I have suggested that production of aluminium should be increased from 4,000 tons to 40,000 tons per year in the Second Plan to supply a base for the development of electricity and for other purposes. In the field of agriculture and animal husbandry it was considered more important to improve the nutritional quality of the diet than to increase the total intake of calories. Similar considerations prevailed in deciding many other targets. It is neither possible nor necessary to describe them in detail.

4. There were also supplementary considerations of a much broader type. I am using the phrase "supplementary considerations" as a concise term for all those different arguments or reasons which we recognize to have some bearing on the methods or targets of planning which should be adopted to attain our objectives. That is, we are working within a general frame work of social, political, economic, and cultural values with some (clearly or vaguely) recognized aims and objectives. Once we accept this frame work as given, it becomes necessary to incorporate in the plan all considerations which are likely to help in attaining the desired objectives.

5. The theoretical model which I have used does not, and cannot obviously, incorporate all these supplementary considerations.

In our view, the proper function of the theoretical model is to supply some broad general guidance leaving the details to be settled from supplementary considerations.* This gives flexibility to the approach, and the scope to adjust the details in accordance with priorities to be reached by agreement through discussions. It is also clear that the theoretical model (being purely technological in character) is necessarily neutral to questions of social or administrative policy. Here also we must give proper attention to methods which are likely to be of help in attaining the desired objectives. That is, it is necessary continually to refer to what I have called the "supplementary considerations" in making decisions about the Plan-frame.

6. Some of these wider considerations have been indicated in the Plan-frame and some others are given in the Joint Secretariat paper or the memorandum prepared by the Panel of Economists. It is not necessary to repeat them here. In view of the importance of industries, I have made certain observations on the future programme of industrial development in the next chapter. Here I may give some other examples.

7. Consider health services. There are at present about 65,000 fully qualified (six-year trained) doctors in India. Most of the doctors reside in urban areas; and it is believed that in the rural areas there is, on an average, only one qualified doctor for twenty thousand persons. Even this distribution is not uniform. In some States the proportion is probably much smaller. About two thousand six-year trained doctors are turned out in India every year, and the cost of training each doctor is about forty or fifty thousand rupees. Under existing conditions it may take 60 or 70 years to provide one doctor for every two thousand persons in the rural areas on an average (a modest target compared to one doctor for 700 or 800 or 1000 persons in USSR, or UK, or USA).

---

* I find simple models useful in planning (just as the thermo-dynamical approach is useful in physics) in revealing the broad characteristics of the system under consideration without getting lost in the details It is clearly out of question to use any complicated model in India in the near future. Statistical data and other factual material are much too meagre. However, when reliable information in great detail becomes available for a very large number of industries or sectors, and also when a great deal of experience has been gathered about the effect of various actions taken in a planned economy, it may become possible to reach quite good solutions to practical problems of planning without any recourse to mathematical models. This is what seems to have happened in the USSR where planning problems are solved with the help of a vast amount of detailed and up-to-date statistics and the use of "balances" (basically something like input-output analysis), but without any mathematical models.

9

I have thought it desirable, therefore, to include in the Draft Plan-frame a proposal to bring some health service to every home in the country within a reasonable time, possibly in 10 or 15 years (instead of providing an exclusively high quality service to a very small fraction of the population), by establishing two new cadres of 2-year and 4-year trained health assistants as a first step to a national health service throughout the country. In addition to public health duties these health assistants would be given training to provide routine treatment in minor ailments. One 6-year trained physician would be in charge of a group of 5 or 6 health assistants; the latter would be provided with bicycles and would be instructed to contact the physician in difficult cases. The cost of training the health assistants would be much less. Also, it would be possible to turn out twelve or fifteen thousand health assistants per year so that one health assistant could be placed in charge of, say, every five villages in the course of about 10 or 12 or 15 years. At the same time, the number of 6-year trained should, of course, continue to be increased as fast as possible.

8. Let us consider another example: improvement in the efficiency of Government machinery. Our theoretical model is neutral because it does not include any variable or parameter corresponding to the type or the efficiency of the administrative machinery. It is our knowledge of the defects and delays of the existing system, and our general appreciation of the level of efficiency which would have to be attained in the management of large Government enterprises that make us think that proper implementation of the plan would be practically impossible without a thorough decentralization of administrative and financial powers. In future the efficiency of public enterprises must be judged on results; and suitable incentives must be offered to increase efficiency. Our appreciation of future possibilities is based partly on the experience of other countries; but obviously, a good deal of experimentation will have to be done to evolve a system suited to Indian conditions and requirements.

9. The recommendations in the Plan-frame on the training programme is very general. There is urgent need of much detailed work being done, on the basis of technical coefficients, to formulate the requirements of technicians at various levels and to formulate appropriate training programmes to meet the demand.

10. Also consider the important question of the respective shares of the public and the private sectors in the new enterprises which

would be started during the Second Plan. Our theoretical model does not and cannot say that a particular industry should be included in the public sector, while some other industry should be included in the private sector. Our basic recommendations in this matter are guided by the need of general Government control over the entire economy of the country. This is also in keeping with the Industrial Policy Resolution of the Government of India of 1948, reaffirmed in December 1954, and is in keeping with the resolution of the Lok Sabha of December 1954 and the Avadi resolution on socialistic pattern adopted by the Congress Party in January 1955.

11. Again, consider the question of raising adequate financial resources for investment. Our theoretical model cannot give any specific guidance. Our recommendations are based on preliminary studies made by experts in public finance; but it is only proper to admit that much detailed studies would have to be undertaken in this field in the immediate future.* At this stage, our main task has been to work out a tentative solution in real terms, leaving it to the financial experts to work out the details of the monetary counterpart. We have taken our stand on the obviously true proposition that if something can be shown to be feasible in physical terms, then the financial and fiscal machinery can always be adjusted to supply a satisfactory monetary counterpart (provided there is no difficulty in making necessary institutional changes). I agree that models should be elaborated to include the monetary counterpart. This would enable us to set targets not only of production but also of the price level. Until this is done other *ad hoc* methods have to be used.

12. I would like to recapitulate the basic features of the Planframe. We start with a given total investment over the plan period (Rs. 5,600 crores), a given rise of national income (5 per cent per year), and an assigned large volume of new employment to be created (110 lakhs) during the plan period together with a steady improvement of income in future. Our solution indicates a large increase in investment in industries producing investment goods, a small rise in investment in factory industries producing consumer goods, considerable activation of all capital-light small and

---

* It is necessary, in my view, to broaden the base of taxation by introducing taxes on capital gains, wealth, and expenditure and by extending and increasing customs and excise duties. The two objectives should be first, to raise adequate financial resources; and, secondly, to remove disparities of opportunities and of level of living.

household enterprises, and a fairly large increase in various services. This solution is not intuitively obvious, and depends both on the validity of the analytical methods used as well as on the approximate accuracy of the values of the parameters adopted. The advantage of putting the whole thing in this form is that the reader can check the validity of the solution.

CHAPTER 6

INDUSTRIAL DEVELOPMENT

BASIC HEAVY INDUSTRIES

1. India has very little of heavy industries for the production
of investment goods; this sector contributes something like perhaps
one per cent to national income.   The Plan-frame has stressed the
need of establishing and expanding the basic industries to manufacture heavy machinery with all possible speed.   This would enable
India to instal new plants for the production of steel, cement, and
other investment goods with the help of machinery manufactured in India out of domestic resources and to produce in increasing quantities machiery required for mineral prospecting and
mining, hydro-electric projects, electrical appliances, railways and
other forms of transport, and for the production of consumer goods
generally.   India has bigger reserves of high quality iron ore than
any other country of the world (three times more than either the USA
or the USSR) and also coal and large possibilities of increasing the
production of electricity.   The object of expanding the basic heavy
industries would be the continuing expansion in future of the
production of both investment and consumer goods with the help
of modern machinery driven by power.

2. This would require a large amount of capital goods much of
which will have to be imported in the beginning.   India's present
dependence on imports of capital goods is a fundamental structural
weakness which must be corrected as quickly as possible.   It would
be obviously more economical from the national point of view
to produce in India as much heavy machinery as possible because
this would ensure a supply of capital goods which would make
India increasingly independent of imports and would strengthen
India's position in the world market.   In my opinion, the development of the heavy machine building industry is so important that,
if necessary, targets of even steel, coal, or transport should be reduced to give higher priority to heavy machines because this would
facilitate a much quicker rate of industrialization after four or
five years.

3. The heavy machinery industry should be in the public sector.
For rapid industrialization of an under-developed country it would

be desirable to keep the cost of capital goods as low as possible. The further removed the type of capital goods under consideration is from the production of final consumer goods, the greater is the need of keeping the price low. Heavy machinery which would manufacture machinery to produce investment goods is the furthest removed from the consumption end. It is essential, therefore, that Government should have complete control over the heavy machinery industry so as to be able to fix prices to suit national needs. Such control would enable Government to shape the future pattern of industrialization through a properly planned programme of production of heavy machinery. If imports are properly regulated, it would be also possible to influence the pattern of investment in the private sector through Government policy in respect of the production and price of heavy machinery for that sector.

4. It is neither necessary nor desirable that India should try to become completely self-sufficient in the production of machinery. India should, however, acquire both the means of production and technical knowledge to be able, if and when necessary, to manufacture essential investment goods within the country. This is necessary for economic independence. But under normal conditions India should continue to purchase abroad such machinery and capital goods as it would not be economic from a national point of view to manufacture in India. On the other hand, India should also develop in the course of time the production of specialized machinery for which there would be an external market. The policy should be to encourage both imports and exports of machinery and capital goods which would be of mutual benefit to India and other countries.

5. In the field of mechanized production India should encourage automation, that is, the use of automatic and electronically controlled machines, to the fullest extent possible. There would be many advantages. The requirements of highly trained and experienced technical personnel would be appreciably reduced which would save much expense on training and, what is more important, would also save a good deal of time. The high quality of the product would be automatically maintained and would reduce rejections and waste. Production would proceed at a uniform rate which would facilitate working out integrated programmes. The capital cost of automation would be, of course, much higher which may, however, be partly or wholly offset by savings on account of training and elimination of wastage. One serious disadvantage would

be the greater rigidity of an automatized system of production in which it would be difficult to introduce improvements of technique in a piecemeal fashion. The automatized system, even if only obsolete in parts, would have to be either scrapped or continued without any change. In spite of such difficulties India may benefit much by the use of automation from an early date, and possibilities in this direction should be continually explored.

SMALL-SCALE AND HOUSEHOLD PRODUCTION

6. The long-term aim would be to use as quickly as possible the most technologically advanced machinery for the production of both investment and consumer goods. This is not immediately possible because of the lack of a sufficiently broad base of heavy industries. It is, therefore, necessary to plan for a transition phase, in which preference would be given to capital-light and labour-intensive small scale and household industries to create as much employment as possible in the immediate future and, at the same time, to release capital resources for the heavy industries. However, as the economy expands and employment increases the need of giving preference to labour-intensive but low-efficiency production would decrease. As the supply of power, machinery and other capital goods increases, a gradual and steady change-over would be made to more efficient forms of production by the increasing use of machinery driven by power.

POLICY OF GREATEST DISPERSAL OF PRODUCTION

7. It is, however, neither necessary nor desirable to copy the developments in the more advanced countries of America and Europe and concentrate production in large factories. On the contrary, the wise policy in India, in my opinion, would be to adopt a policy of the greatest dispersal of industrial production.

8. This would, of course, include geographical dispersal, that is, locating units of production in such a way that the different regions of India can share equitably in the programme of production. Specialized regional resources and economy of transport must receive proper consideration; but planning should be deliberately aimed at achieving a broad parity in the level of production and of living in the different regions of India and preventing the formation of depressed areas.

9. But this is not all. It would be desirable to try to classify all industries into two broad groups. One, in which the physical

scale of production would have to be large; for example, steel, cement, railway rolling stock, fertilizers, heavy machinery, motor cars, antibiotics, etc. In such cases large factories must be established. It would be desirable to do this in well-planned new industrial towns with adequate housing, schools, medical clinics, hospitals, and facilities for sports and cultural activities not only for the workers employed directly in the planned factories but also for other people who would come to live in the new town for subsidiary occupations. The capital cost of large and medium factories established in this way would be high but the additional expenditure would be a social obligation.

10. The second type of industries would be that in which production is technologically possible in small units. In the case of these industries preference should be given to the smallest units which are economical from the point of view of the nation as a whole. Consider, for example, the traditional highly skilled artistic handicrafts of India such as, Banaras or Patola textiles, Kashmir shawls, silver and gold work, metal work of Moradabad or Bidri, ivory and wood carving, Midnapore and Masalipatam mats, artistic leather work, etc.; every one would agree that India should try to preserve and encourage these handicrafts. There is a good deal of scope and need of improving efficiency of production by developing specialized small tools driven by power which would lighten the manual labour. There is no reason, for example, why a metal box should not be pressed out by machinery and the artistic part of the work done by hand. Efforts should be made to improve the design from a functional point of view and to introduce standards of quality.

11. I have much more in view. I believe it would be possible to produce economically in small units many articles which are now manufactured in large factories. The large factories at present enjoy certain facilities which are not available to small scale and household enterprises. The most important advantage is the use of machinery driven by power. If a policy of dispersal is deliberately adopted then arrangements would be made to supply modern machinery driven by power to the small scale and household enterprises. There is no inherent reason why all efficient machines should be large. With the growth of capitalism, as big factories began to be established in large numbers, the mind of the inventor was more and more directed to large units of production which would suit the big factories because such factories (and not small producers)

were in a position to offer large financial incentives for new inventions which would increase their efficiency of production. Under capitalism the trend of inventions was, therefore, towards large units. The increasing use of electronic technology has, however, already changed the direction of invention towards smaller machines in many fields. Also, in large factories in many cases, machines are comparatively small in size and are looked after by one or two persons. In such cases it is even now possible to set up small independent units of production. Under planning incentives can be offered for the invention of small but efficient machines.

12. Secondly, large factories are usually able to raise capital or borrow money at low rates of interest, purchase raw materials at competitive prices, and enjoy good facilities for marketing which are often under their direct control. The small scale and household enterprises are greatly handicapped in this respect. They have difficulty in securing credit and even when they are able to borrow money, they are obliged to pay high rates of interest. Their supply of raw materials and tools is uncertain; also they are sometimes obliged to pay unreasonably high prices. They have very little marketing facilities; and are usually exploited by middlemen. If Government can arrange to supply credit, raw materials, and marketing facilities to the small scale and household industries then their efficiency of production would be much improved, and they would be able to compete with large factories in many cases.

13. The large factories also enjoy many external economies the cost of which is borne by the tax-payer. Most of the large factories are located in or near large towns and cities; and the factory owners usually do not offer housing, education, medical care and other amenities for their workers. There are, of course, exceptions; but by and large most of the privately owned factories depend on the public authorities for such facilities. The cost of roads, water, electricity, drainage, transport are not charged to the factories. If the large investments required for such purposes as well as maintenance expenses are taken into consideration then it may be found in many cases that the social cost of factory production is much higher than the cost as it appears in the factory accounts. In addition there are intangible costs which cannot be expressed in terms of money such as the misery of slum life, evils arising from the workers having to live away from their families, and other adverse social repercussions. If all economic, social and human costs of large factories are properly taken into account,

10

in many cases it would be preferable, from the point of view of the nation as a whole, to substitute production in small scale and household enterprises.

14. As electricity begins to reach the villages (or with the help of small steam or diesel engines) it would be also possible gradually to convert the small and household enterprises in the villages into high efficiency and low cost mechanized units of production. This would avoid the heavy expenses which would be incurred for urbanization if the same production had to be arranged in large factories. There would be also large savings in transport and other overheads.

15. In small cooperatives or in self-employed household enterprises the workers would be able to work much longer hours than in factories; also, some of the members of the household would do part-time work so that there would be practically double shift operation. Working at home or very near home in the villages would be less fatiguing than in factories because the workers would be able to take some rest as and when necessary. Household activities and family life would not be disrupted.

16. Dispersal of production in small units in villages or small towns would be particularly suited to social and economic conditions in this country. India has many geographical, linguistic and ethnic regions with large differences in climate, food habits and social customs. It is difficult to transfer surplus labour from one part of the country to another. There is practically no migration from villages in one region to villages in other regions. Labourers come from villages to work in towns and cities; but a good number is seasonal who go back to their villages at the time of peak loads of agriculture. If mechanized industrial occupations can be established in the country, many of the labourers would stay in or near villages which would ensure an adequate supply of agricultural labour at peak-loads. This would be of great help in the transition phase. The policy of dispersal would tend to raise the level of living in villages and remove the present large disparities between rural and urban areas. For all these reasons it is desirable to adopt a deliberate policy of "back to the village" in, however, a new form in which electricity (or small steam or diesel engines) and modern machinery would be supplied to the village for industrial production.

17. The future policy, in my opinion, should be to establish and bring all large units of production under direct Government control; to develop enterprises of a medium size on a cooperative

basis; and leave small units of production to household enterprises. Such a policy of dispersal would have political advantages. It would tend to create a large number of household or small scale enterprises which would be organized more and more in the form of cooperatives and would supply a sound foundation for a democratic society. It would avoid, on one hand, the disadvantages of heavy concentration of financial power in the hands of a small number of monopoly capitalists; and, on the other hand, would also avoid the rigidities of a highly centralized, bureaucratic administration. Through a policy of industrial dispersal it would be possible to combine the advantages of both economic and political democracy in an effective manner. This would be a solution entirely in keeping with Indian social and cultural traditions.

CHAPTER 7

CONCLUDING REMARKS

The first draft of this paper was written in June 1955 and was revised in short intervals between frequent journeys both in India and abroad. Originally it was my intention to give a much fuller account of the implications of the approach to planning adopted in the Plan-frame. I prepared drafts of a number of other chapters but I have not had time to complete them. In the meantime I am making some brief observations on different aspects of planning in India.

2. In the Plan-frame we started with the allocation of investments with a view to realizing the given targets of production. A programme of production which is consistent internally in respect of requirements of men, machinery and materials and is also capable of realizing the desired targets of income and employment is, however, not enough. The raising of financial resources required for this purpose is equally important. It is, therefore, necessary to work out a programme of public finance. The present system of taxes and public finance is based on the model of industrially advanced capitalist societies. Much fresh thinking would be needed to develop a scheme of taxation and monetary measures which would be suitable for an under-developed country like India, from the point of view of both economic growth and social justice. In India less than half a million (five lakhs) persons pay income-tax. Assuming an average size of a family of seven for each person paying income-tax, the total number of persons directly affected would be about three and a half million (35 lakhs) or less than one per cent of the total population. This one per cent owns a disproportionately large share of the wealth of the whole country. It would be desirable, from the point of view of social justice, to raise financial resources for the plan by taxation rather than by borrowings or deficit financing which, under existing conditions in India, are likely to increase the profits of those who are already rich. The direct tax can be appreciably increased by suitable changes in the structure of the income tax, and by imposing taxes on capital gains and wealth. It is also possible to introduce a progressive direct tax on personal expenditure at low rates and with a high exemption

limit.* Even this is not likely to be enough to supply the large resources needed for a rapid growth of the economy. Additional resources can be secured through indirect taxes by raising customs and excise duties in a selective manner. The tax on luxuries can be increased very considerably so as to reduce disparities in the level of living. Essential commodities may also have to be taxed to raise adequate resources; but this should not be a hardship as the income of the majority of the population, who are poor, would increase rapidly with the increase of employment and work. All this would require a good deal of careful study.

3. It is comparatively easy to prepare plans on paper; the real difficulty lies in implementing them. Suitable instruments and techniques of implementation must be devised to realize the targets. It will be necessary to formulate and give effect to a vast programme of training of personnel at all levels. There will be urgent and continuing need of scientific and technological research oriented towards solving problems of national planning. This is essentially a long range task and it would be necessary to think in terms of 15 or 20 years and more.

4. The present system of education aims at providing very detailed teaching and instructions spread over a long period for a very small number of persons who are rich enough to pay for such education or who have the ability to win scholarships. The need for this type of education would continue; and educational facilities of the conventional type will have to be increased as rapidly as possible. But this would not be enough. A new approach will be necessary. Here the aim would be to give very quick training to a very large number of persons to enable them to start functioning as junior or auxiliary technicians in engineering and technology, agriculture, survey of natural resources, education, and health services. Suitable packaged and highly specialized courses would have to be developed for this purpose; and the training would have to be given not only in training schools and institutions but also, in an increasing measure, in factories, mines, irrigation and power projects, farms, and in hospitals and clinics all over the country. The selection of students for different types of training would require careful planning. Appropriate tests and examinations would have to be developed for this purpose. Much study and experimentation would be required to prepare the highly specialized short courses. It would be also useful to provide facilities

* N. Kaldor: *An Expenditure Tax* (Allen and Unwin, London, 1955).

for training through correspondence courses which can be made available to remote villages.

5. Much thought will have to be given to improve the efficiency of public enterprises. Government administration has been so far concerned primarily with work of a quasi-judicial type in which decisions may affect a large number of people. It is important to avoid wrong decisions. It is also important to reconcile conflicting views among different Government agencies. There is no special hurry as there is no productive activity in the economic sense. All these call for much consultation and it is safe to have checks and cross-checks at different levels. The emphasis is on "control" in the sense of preventing mistakes or wilful deviations from prescribed rules and "coordination" in the sense of eliminating duplications or adjudicating between conflicting points of view of different agencies. The basic assumption is that the purpose in view would be fulfilled if there is no deviation from the rules.

6. In Government enterprises, on the other hand, the sole purpose is to manufacture specified products or to provide specified services (as in trading). In this case the real test of efficiency is an objective appraisal of the output of the final product or services. Mere adherence to rules cannot guarantee the fulfilment of the targets of production. The public enterprises must be given sufficient autonomy to realize their production targets on businesslike lines. Much study and experimentation would be needed to evolve a suitable system of decentralization of the administrative and financial powers of public enterprises within the general frame work of a planned economy. This would naturally involve important questions of recruitment, control and promotion of personnel; incentives to promote efficiency; relationships between Government, management, labour, and consumer, etc. Competence of government officials must be judged on results, literally, on the ability to deliver the goods, and must be suitably recognized.

7. The Government of India had carried on trading in grains on a large scale for about ten years (1943-1952). It is likely that Government would have to take up trading again and gradually to increase the scale of operations. The State Bank is being expanded with a view to providing credit to rural areas on a large scale. Suitable institutions will have to be organized for the further expansion of Government trading and banking. Thought will have to be given to the expansion of foreign trade and the earning of foreign exchange for which a good deal of planning will be needed.

8. Attention will have to be given to land policy. Most of the States have acquired from the landlords the large holdings of land through legislation but very little has been done for the redistribution of the acquired land. One view is that a maximum size of the holding (depending on local conditions) should be fixed and land in excess of the ceiling should be distributed among villagers who do not own or have very little land. Such redistribution would not necessarily lead to an increase in productivity but it may still be worthwhile because of the social and political benefits which would accrue from it. However, if such a redistribution be not immediately feasible then attempts should be made for a gradual consolidation of holdings with some kind of joint ownership. The success of the *Bhoodan* movement of Acharya Vinoba Bhave, who is advocating joint cultivation of the village as a whole, may be of great help in this connexion. The introduction of mechanized production in agriculture would probably have to come at a later stage when an adequate supply of power and of agricultural machinery manufactured within the country becomes available. With an increase in income the demand for food of better quality (vegetables, eggs, fish, meat, milk and milk-products, fruits etc.) would steadily increase. The pattern of agricultural production would have to be changed for this purpose which would require planning over a period of 20 or 30 years and more.

9. Other aspects of implementation would require attention. However well thought out a plan-programme may be, it is inevitable that shortfalls and deviations would occur in practice. The original programme itself would be based, in many respects, on inadequate or even incorrect information. Changes would also continually occur through the impact of the private sector (which is very large in India) and economic conditions outside India. There would be delays in the process of production which would lead to shortages of machinery, raw materials and labour or of consumer goods from time to time. A most important task of planning must be to introduce controls and take corrective measures at the earliest opportunity. A great deal of advance thinking and preparation is necessary for this purpose. For example, it would be wise to have a fully worked out scheme (and also, preferably, a nucleus organization) for the rationing of commodities like grains, cloth, sugar etc., so that, if any emergency arises, there would be no delay in introducing physical controls. Similar preparatory work would have to be done in other fields like finance, foreign trade, supply

of machinery, raw materials and labour, training programmes, and administrative arrangements.

10. A good system of statistical services is essential for the preparation of plan-programmes as well as for an objective appraisal of the results achieved. There must be a continuing flow of statistical information from all sectors of the economy and from all over the country to enable a proper assessment being made of the progress of the plant not only in terms of expenditure but in terms of fulfilment of physical targets and of increase in the volume of employment and of the rise in the level of living. On the basis of such assessment it would be possible to introduce controls and corrective measures at appropriate points and to make necessary adjustments in the future programme.

11. The type of planning visualized above would be necessarily a continuing process and would have two broad aspects. One would be the current planning directed to projects included in the annual plans within the frame work of a five year plan. The successive five-year plans themselves would have to be fitted into a larger frame work of perspective planning with a wide time horizon of 10 or 20 or 30 years or even more. Perspective planning would be primarily concerned with the technical and scientific aspects of the long-term growth of the economy. Studies and researches would be directed to solving practical problems and would be broadly of the type of "operational research" (although some problems of basic research would no doubt arise from time to time). This would call for the active cooperation of a large number of engineers, technologists, economists, statisticians, and workers in practically all fields of both natural and social sciences.

ACKNOWLEDGEMENTS

12. I have already mentioned that the "Draft Plan-frame" was prepared for issue, after revision, as a document of the Planning Commission but it was actually published in my name. The Draft Plan-frame is, in fact, a cooperative effort and is based on studies on planning conducted in the Indian Statistical Institute in collaboration with the Economic Division of the Planning Commission, the Economic Division of the Finance Ministry, and the Central Statistical Organization. A large number of persons participated in these studies and a number of working papers were produced. A part of this material has been used in the Plan-frame and this paper; other studies have no direct relation with the Plan-frame.

All these working papers are going to be printed in the near future. A very brief account of the work done is given below.

13. Professor Charles Bettelheim of France developed a particular method of planning in his papers. His approach may be regarded as a synthesis of the methods of planning followed in socialized countries. He, of course, tried to adapt the methods to Indian conditions. His approach has a good deal in common with the approach of the Plan-frame in regard to the setting up of the targets and the working out of the physical balances. The allocation of investments in the Plan-frame, however, has an entirely different basis. About finances, also, the Plan-frame approach is different. Apart from this, Professor Bettelheim initiated some studies on capacity of production with a view to estimating the additional raw materials and other things which would be required, if the capacity is to be fully utilized; co-efficients calculated for this purpose were found useful for working out the requirements of raw materials for some of the targets given in the Plan-frame. The following workers were actively associated with the studies initiated by Professor Bettelheim; Asoke Rudra, E. Lobel, A. Qayum, Uma Dutta, Probir Das, P. K. Upadhyay, R. L. Rawat, Nikhilesh Bhattacharya, Pranbandhu Das, G. R. Vernwal, G. V. L. Narasinham and Sashi Chakravarty.

14. Professor Ragnar Frisch of Norway pursued studies based on fairly elaborate transactions matrices. Given such a matrix he would maximize a suitable preference function subject to the constraints given by the relations in the matrix and some boundary conditions. Once a reliable matrix of this kind is available and a suitable preference function can be constructed, his method would give, in principle, a solution of the problem of development. The statistical material available in India is, however, not adequate to enable this method being used with success at present; and his work, at this stage, remains primarily of methodological interest. It may be noted that he obtained his linear programming solutions by his double gradient method and demonstrated its superiority over the simplex method in so far as time requirement is concerned. The following workers were associated with Professor Frisch: Tarapada Chaudhuri, Dev Kumar Bose, Amal Ray and Ajit Halder.

15. Dr. Richard M. Goodwin of Cambridge, England and Dr. Tarapada Chaudhuri prepared an input-output table relating to 1950-51. Material for this purpose was extracted by a quick tabulation of a sub-sample of the National Sample Survey and was

11

used to estimate the overall activity and the sector break-down of costs. The Central Statistical Organization collaborated by supplying detailed information relating to estimates of national income. Work is continuing in this field in the Indian Statistical Institute and recently a larger input-output table for 1951-52 has been completed. Prominent workers in this group were: Tarapada Chaudhuri, Indra Chakravarti, Amiya Dasgupta, Kalpana Joshi, Ashish Chakravarti, Samar Mitra, H.P. Biswas, Prasanta Chowdhury, D. V. R. Murti, B. P. Panesar and Sunil Sinha. Subsequently, Satya Sengupta and his associates worked on studies of a similar type.

16. Jogabrata Roy, Indra Chakravarti, Radha Govinda Laha, A. Ganguly, Shyam Bose and Sukomal Das worked on the problem of projection of consumption and obtained some estimates of elasticities. Their results have been used in the Plan-frame.

17. Ajit Dasgupta worked on the problem of population projection and obtained estimates of projected population under different hypotheses. His group included among others: Murari Majumdar, Ranjan Som, B. N. Sarkar, Dhiren Sarkar and Prosun Sen.

18. Sitanghsu Bhattacharya and Ram Lingam Iyer made some studies on manufacturing industries. Certain field studies on unemployment, and interactions between planned and unplanned sectors were taken up by N. C. Ghosh, H. K. Chaturvedi, Keshav Dutt, Prosun Sen and Sudhir Bhattacharya.

19. Nihar Chakravarti wrote a paper on a plan of land reform. Raja Rao, R. P. Saha, Haribhajan Chowdhury and subsequently G. Kallianpur worked on certain aspects of the problem of land reform.

20. D. B. Lahiri aided by Saibal Banerjee, S. J. Poti, Samar Mitra, Des Raj and Sambhu Halder worked on the general question of the validity of data. D. B. Lahiri subsequently helped in administrative matters relating to planning. C. R. Rao helped in our work by placing the facilities of the Research and Training School at our diposal for these studies. B. Ramamurti (Jt. Director, CSO) assisted by M. P. Srivastava (Asst. Director, CSO) supplied necessary statistical data from the Central Statistical Organization and made its facilities generally available for these studies.

21. J. J. Anjaria (Chief, Economic Division, Planning Commission and Economic Adviser, Ministry of Finance) and I. G. Patel (Deputy Economic Adviser, Ministry of Finance) worked out the financial and monetary side; and generally helped in the preparation of the Plan-frame. Moni Mukherjee (Deputy Director, CSO) and Uma Dutta (of the CSO) worked on my two-sector model and helped

me in following up some of my ideas which culminated in the preparation of the Plan-frame. Pitambar Pant (Deputy Secretary, and
Private Secretary to the Chairman, Planning Commission) helped
at all stages of the work.

22. Academician D. D. Degtyar, Professor I. Y. Pisarev, M. I.
Rubinstein and P. A. Moskvin of U.S.S.R. and Dr. Oskar Lange
of Poland gave a critical appraisal of the general approach and the
final form of the Draft Plan-frame on the basis of their own
experience of socialized economies. Their comments and observations were of great help to us although our own approach is
different from theirs in certain important respects. The aim of
the Plan-frame has been to seek an approach which would be
suited to Indian needs and would be in accordance with the social
and cultural traditions of India.

REFERENCES

(1) CHAMPERNOWNE, D. G. and KAHN, R. F. (1953-54) : The Value of Invested
Capital. *The Review of Economic Studies*, XXI (2), No. 55.

(2) GOVERNMENT OF INDIA : Estimates of National Income, 1948-49 to 1953-54
(Central Statistical Organization, 1951).

(3) ———— : Fifth Census of Indian Manufactures : 1950. (Directorate of
Industrial Statistics, Ministry of Commerce & Industry).

(4) ———— : The National Sample Survey, Report No. 1. (Department of
Economic Affairs, Ministry of Finance).

(5) ———— : India, A Reference Annual 1955. (Ministry of Information &
Broadcasting).

(6) ———— : First Five Year Plan, 1951–56 (Planning Commission).

(7) ———— : Programmes of Industrial Development, 1951–56 (Planning
Commission, 1953).

(8) ———— : Five Year Plan, Progress Report for 1953-54 (Planning Commission, 1954).

(9) GOVERNMENT OF WEST BENGAL : Economic Survey of Small-Scale Industries
of Calcutta, 1952-53. (State Statistical Bureau, 1954).

(10) GOVERNMENT OF USA : Survey of Current Business, July 1953. (Department of Commerce, Washington, D.C.).

(11) HALDANE, J. B. S. : The Maximization of National Income. *Sankhyā*,
Vol. 16, Parts I and II.

(12) KUZNETS, SIMON : National Income and its Composition, 1919–1938.
(National Bureau of Economic Research, New York, 1946).

(13) ———— : National Product since 1869. (National Bureau of Economic
Research, New York, 1946).

(14) ———— (1952) : Economic Growth in the United States. *American Economic
Review*, XLII, No. 2, May.

(15) LENFANT, J. H. : Great Britain's Capital Formation, 1865–1914. (*Economica*,
May, 1951).

(16) MAHALANOBIS, P. C. : "Why Statistics ?" (Presidential Address to the
Indian Science Congress Session, Poona, 1950).

(17) ———— : National Income, Investment, and National Development. Lecture
at the National Institute of Sciences, 4 October 1952.

(18) ———— (1953) : Some Observations on the Process of Growth of National
Income. *Sankhyā*, **12**, Part 4.

(19) PREST, A. R. (1948) : National Income of the United Kingdom, 1870–1946.
         The Economic Journal.

(20) RESERVE BANK OF INDIA : Company Finances in India, 1950 and 1951.
         (*Bulletin*, August, 1954).

(21) SURVEY OF SMALL SCALE INDUSTRIES : Bureau of Industrial Statistics,
         Calcutta, 1954.

(22) UNITED NATIONS : Report on World Survey of Iron Ore Deposits (1955).

(23) ————— : A System of National Accounts and Supporting Tables (1953).

(24) ————— : Statistics of National Income and Expenditure, Statistical
         Papers, Series H, No. 7.

(25) ————— : Economic Survey of Asia and the Far East, 1954 (1955).

RECOMMENDATIONS FOR THE FORMULATION OF THE SECOND FIVE YEAR PLAN

Prime Minister Jawaharlal Nehru inaugurated the studies relating to planning for national development in the Indian Statistical Institute on 3 November 1954. The work on economic planning was then organized and carried on with the active collaboration of the Central Statistical Organization, the Economic Division of the Planning Commission and the Department of the Economic Affairs of the Ministry of Finance. On the basis of four agency co-operative studies the 'Draft Plan-Frame' was prepared and submitted to the Prime Minister on 17 March 1955. The Panel of Economists, Planning Commission examined the 'Draft' in April 1955 which was then accepted by the National Development Council in May 1955 as the basis for the formulation of the Second Five Year Plan of India.

PREFACE

1. The paper dated March 17, 1955 was prepared as a *draft of a " draft Plan-frame"* and has been circulated as such and is subject to revision by the Planning Commission.

2. The general objectives and policy and administrative questions (which are discussed in Chapters One and Six) can be considered on their own merits.

3.1. The quantitative estimates were worked out with two chief aims in view, namely,

(a) an increase in national income of 5 per cent per year; and

(b) creation of new employment by way of gainful occupation or jobs for 11 million persons over the plan period.

3.2. Certain basic allocations of investments were made between investment goods and consumer goods industries. It is necessary to maintain this general pattern of investments but there is scope for adjustments in details.

3.3. The draft Plan-frame is, therefore, not rigid and can be modified; but there are inter-relations between its different parts so that a change of the target in one item may require consequential changes in other items.

4.1. Background information relating to the physical targets and financial estimates (Chapters Two, Three, Four and Five) will be found in the accompanying paper prepared jointly by the

Economic Division of the Planning Commission, the Economic Division of the Ministry of Finance, the Central Statistical Organization, and the Indian Statistical Institute.

4.2. The draft of the draft Plan-frame and the above joint paper are consistent with each other but are not identical.

4.3. The Report of the Panel of Economists dated 10 April 1955 has reference to both the above papers.

5.1. Within the general pattern of investments (explained in para 3), an attempt was made to fit in the physical targets on the basis of information that was readily available in the Planning Commission and in the Ministries concerned.

5.2. The draft Plan-frame does not attempt to go into details. In some cases, information was not available; and time was short. Also, it was not necessary to make the list of targets exhaustive or complete in every respect because, as explained in para 3, there is scope for adjustments in details without disturbing the main structure of the Plan-frame.

6.1. The targets are sometimes given as equivalent aggregates within which there can be substitution of components.

6.2. Estimates of financial outlay are to be taken as *net*.

6.3. Construction costs are to be taken as the direct costs of materials, of labour, and of essential technical supervision. It is assumed that excessive margins for intermediaries and other forms of waste will be eliminated.

6.4. It is assumed that promotional and field agencies and services would be integrated and coordinated to prevent unnecessary duplication.

6.5. It is assumed that non-official public organizations would be used wherever possible to decrease overhead expenses and stimulate public interest and participation in the fulfilment of the Plan.

7.1. If the basic approach of the present draft is approved, it is suggested that the paper should be revised as necessary and then issued in the revised form as the *draft* Plan-frame for the formulation of projects.

7.2. After the individual projects are received, further changes and adjustments should be made as necessary to get ready, as quickly as possible, a definitive plan which would be internally consistent and would be capable of attaining the desired objectives.

28th April 1955   P. C. Mahalanobis

INTRODUCTION

1.1. The Second Five Year Plan is due to begin on April 1, 1956. The approach in the Second Five Year Plan is to take a perspective view of development over a long period of years, and at the same time to solve immediate problems like unemployment as quickly as possible. Planning would be, therefore, flexible and would always keep a wide time horizon in view; and at the same time detailed annual plans would be prepared and necessary adjustments made at shorter intervals in the light of experience.

1.2. Proper attention must be given to the physical aspects of the Second Five Year Plan. The requirements of each project must be estimated in real terms at the stage of planning and must be forthcoming in right quantities at the right time at the stage of implementation of the project. Also, the products and services resulting from the completion of a project must be fully and promptly utilized to further the execution of other projects and the progress of the plan as a whole.

1.3. A plan in a mixed economy must be comprehensive and cover both the public and the private sectors. To achieve a balanced growth, the activities of the private sector must conform in a general way to the programme of production of the plan as a whole. In an expanding economy the private sector would have an assured market which would facilitate decisions by reducing risks and uncertainties. Also, the over-all programme would be laid down in broad aggregates so that there would be wide scope for adjustments in details at the discretion of the private sector.

1.4. The physical targets of production must also be balanced in terms of money. Incomes are generated in the very process of production; and supplies are utilized through market operations. Planning requires that aggregate incomes should be balanced with expenditure, savings should match investments, and the supply and demand of individual goods and services should be balanced in terms of money so as to avoid any inflationary rise of prices or undesirable shifts in prices. Physical and financial planning are different aspects of the same reality.

2.1. *Plan-frame*: The enclosed paper contains chapters on main aims and objectives; provisional targets of production; investment and development expenditure; expected changes in employment and income; finance and foreign trade; and planning organization and administration to supply a tentative frame-work for the formulation of the Second Five Year Plan.

2.2. It is requested that the Central Ministries, State Governments, and other project-making authorities should use the provisional figures given in the paper as a general Plan-frame for the formulation of schemes and projects taking care to make estimates in both physical and financial terms, and to forward them to the Planning Commission as they become ready.

2.3. When the individual schemes and projects have been received in the Planning Commission, the aggregate balances would be examined and adjusted as necessary until an integrated plan is evolved which will be internally consistent and balanced in both physical and financial terms. Estimates of demand and supply are bound to be approximate to begin with; and would have to be worked and re-worked to secure a proper balance.

2.4. It is recognized that while projects are being prepared there would be need of a two-way flow of information as well as of consultations between project-making bodies and the Planning Commission. The present recommendations would supply the initial base for such consultations and discussions.

3.1. *Time programme* : The programme for the first year (April 1956—March 1957) of the Second Five Year Plan must be completed by October 1955. This first year's programme would contain much carry-over from First Five Year Plan and some new items for which projects are ready or are in an advanced state of preparation. It is requested that projects for 1956-57 (including the carry-over from the First Five Year Plan) should be sent to the Planning Commission as soon as possible.

3.2. The Second Five Year Plan must be ready (in outline form) by March 1956. Projects for the remaining period of Second Five Year Plan should therefore be sent to the Planning Commission as they become ready.

4.1. Some of the projects would have to be submitted necessarily in a general form at the present stage; and working details would be prepared after it is decided that they would be included in the plan. Nevertheless, it is essential that preliminary information should be given in the prescribed form even if the estimates are of an approximate nature because a technical examination of the projects would not be possible in the absence of such information.

4.2. The Planning Commision would be glad to supply further information in this connection and help in the preparation of schemes and projects.

CHAPTER ONE

GENERAL AIMS AND OBJECTIVES

1.1. *The First Five Year Plan*: At the beginning of the First Five Year Plan the country was still dislocated by war and partition. There was shortage of food and raw materials. There were signs of inflationary pressures after hostilities had started in Korea. In this situation it is understandable that the targets of the First Five Year Plan were kept modest. Judged in this context, the progress achieved so far may be regarded as satisfactory.

1.2. There are, however, disquieting features. Agricultural prices are declining. Unemployment, especially in urban areas, is increasing. Even the modest expenditure targets in the First Five Year Plan have not been fully achieved on account of delays in preparing projects, inadequate administrative organization, and lack of sufficient facilities to give training to technical personnel.

2.1. *The need of a bold plan* : The population of India is increasing roughly at the rate of 4.5 million per year. With a proportion of about 40 per cent in the labour force, about 1.8 million persons enter the labour force every year. In addition, a large number of persons are without employment in urban areas and a great deal of under-employment exists in villages. Planning must be bold enough to provide new work for about 1.8 million new entrants into the working force every year; and also to offer more work to the large number of persons who are without jobs or who are under-employed at present.

2.2. The level of living is extremely low. Expenditure on consumer goods per person is about Rs. 22 per month of which about Rs. 13 is spent in cash and about Rs. 9 is the value of consumption of home grown food and home made articles. Housing is primitive in villages and extremely short in urban areas. The supply of nutritive foods is meagre although nearly two-thirds of the total expenditure is spent on food items. The expenditure on education is only about four annas per person per month and on health less than seven annas.

2.3. The above estimates are for all classes taken together. The position of the poorer section is much worse. Half the population of India or 185 million persons spend less than Rs. 13 per month on consumer goods and possibly half of this amount is consumed in kind or in the form of home grown food and home made articles. Of children in the school-going age, less than half attend at the primary stage, and less than one-fifth at the secondary stage. There is probably less than one qualified physician per 30,000 inhabitants in the villages.

3.1. *General objectives of the Second Five Year Plan*: There is a large pool of idle man-power, and many are without jobs; also about 1.8 million persons would be added to the working force every year. The country has large resources of water for hydro-electric and irrigation projects; coal, iron ore and other important minerals; forests, fertile land and cattle. The aim of planning must be to utilize these resources to increase rapidly the level of production and thus of national income.

3.2. Conditions are favourable in many ways. There is economic stability and confidence in Government. Unemployed man-power and unexploited resources can be brought together to increase both consumption and investment simultaneously. India's prestige is high at the international level. Finally the Congress Party and Government have decided that the time has come for economic development on a socialistic pattern.

3.3. The Second Five Year Plan is therefore being formulated with the following objectives in view:

(1) to attain a rapid growth of the national economy by increasing the scope and importance of the public sector and in this way to advance to a socialistic pattern of society;

(2) to develop basic heavy industries for the manufacture of producer goods to strengthen the foundations of economic independence;

(3) to increase the production of consumer goods as much as possible through the household or hand industries ; and to provide an adequate market for the products;

(4) to develop factory production of consumer goods in a way not competitive with hand industries;

(5) to increase productivity in agriculture; and to speed up agrarian reforms with an equitable distribution of land to peasant cultivators so as to stimulate the increase of agricultural production and of purchasing power in rural areas;

(6) to provide better housing, more health services, and greater opportunities for education especially for the poorer sections of the population;

(7) to liquidate unemployment as quickly as possible and within a period not exceeding ten years;

(8) and as the result of such measures to increase national income by about 25 per cent over the plan period and achieve a more equitable distribution of income.

3.4. The basic strategy would be to increase purchasing power through investments in heavy industries in the public sector and through expenditure on health, education, and social services; and to meet the increasing demand for consumer goods by a planned supply of such goods so that there would be no undesirable inflationary pressures. Planning would be thus essentially a feedback process of matching a continuously increasing (planned) demand by a continuously increasing (planned) production giving rise to a steadily expanding economy.

4.1. *Heavy industries* : In the long run, the rate of industrialization and the growth of national economy would depend on the increasing production of coal, electricity, iron and steel, heavy machinery, heavy chemicals, and the heavy industries generally which would increase the capacity for capital formation. One important aim is to make India independent, as quickly as possible, of foreign imports of producer goods so that the accumulation of capital would not be hampered by difficulties in securing supplies of essential producer goods from other countries. The heavy industries must, therefore, be expanded with all possible speed.

4.2. The new producer goods industries would be developed mainly in the public sector. The private sector would continue to play an important part in the development of basic industries like cement, chemicals, etc.

4.3. The heavy industries being capital-intensive would, however, give relatively little scope for employment; and would also generate a large demand for consumer goods which they themselves would not be able to supply.

5.1. *Household and hand industries* : The increasing purchasing power and consequential demand for consumer goods must be met by increasing the supply of such goods as much as possible through the expansion of household or hand production. This would also quickly generate a large volume of work all over the country.

5.2. Construction work (roads, houses, irrigation and flood control projects, etc.) by hand would also be increased which would create a good deal of employment and generate demand for consumer goods,

5.3.   The greater the marketable surplus of consumer goods in the household or hand industries the greater will be the possibilities of investments in heavy industries without any fear of inflation.

5.4.   By expanding the household and hand industries and construction work, the aggregate national consumption would increase continually.   Also, relatively more employment would be created among the poorer sections of the people so that a greater portion of the increase in income would go to them.

6.1.   *Factory production of consumer goods* :   The production of consumer goods in factories requires heavy investment of capital per engaged person and in many cases competes with the household or hand industries.   Until unemployment is liquidated or brought under control, it is necessary to prevent competition between factories and household or hand industries by not permitting investments to be made in such consumer goods factories as would prevent expansion or lead to a shrinkage of employment in the hand industries.

6.2.   In the immediate future the factory production of consumer goods would be expanded (where it is not competitive with hand industries) to increase the supply of essential goods (like antibiotics, fine drugs, etc.) or of goods for export to earn foreign exchange.

6.3.   It is recognised that the price of hand-made goods would often be higher than the price of factory-made goods of comparable quality.   Appropriate excise duties (which would be selective) would be imposed on factory products to maintain desired price parities with hand made goods in such cases.

6.4.   Once mass unemployment has gone, the aim would be to provide cheap power and small machines to the household sector and hand industries to increase productivity per worker and hence the total national product.   At this stage the factory production of consumer goods would also be increased.

7.1.   *Agriculture and allied pursuits* :   The fixation of ceilings and procedural arrangements for the redistribution of land to peasant cultivators must be decided at an early date in each State in accordance with general principles and standards settled on an all India basis, and the redistribution must be completed by 1958. This would make visible important structural changes in the economy resulting in stimulation of agricultural production and provision of a large market for the growing output of industry and handicrafts; and would also transfer a part of the national income from recipients who use it largely for luxurious consumption to recipients who will use it for productive purposes and for raising their low standard of life.

7.2. The National Extension Service Blocks (and Community Projects where possible) would be extended all over the country to help and speed up the improvement of living conditions in rural areas.

7.3. Because of the urgent need of increasing the production of foodstuffs and raw materials, the highest priority would be given to the setting up of a State Bank, as recommended in the Report of the Rural Credit Survey Committee, for the supply of agricultural credit.

7.4. The same or an associated system would be used for the supply of credit, raw materials, and marketing facilities to the household and hand industries through an organization of co-operatives with the support (or the direct participation or partnership) of Government.

7.5. As an increase in the caloric value is not enough for a balanced diet, concerted efforts must be made to increase the supply of food of higher nutritive and protective value such as fruits and vegetables, milk and milk products, eggs, fish, meat etc.

7.6. Continuing efforts must be made to increase the production of milk products by improving the quality of cattle through the introduction of better breeds, by increasing the production of fodder crops and cattle feed, and by providing better veterinary services by increasing the number of trained veterinary surgeons and veterinary assistants.

8. *Health* : There must be a rapid increase in the care of health. A national health service would be established in the rural areas with paid health assistants in charge of a group of villages who would work in contact with fully trained physicians. The number of dispensaries and hospitals, and facilities for medical training would be increased in urban areas.

9.1. *Education* : There must be a rapid increase in literacy, improvement in the pay of teachers, and better organization of education at all levels.

9.2. On the basis of merit, able students, at all levels and in increasing numbers, must be provided with adequate living and educational expenses to enable them to receive education up to the highest standard according to capacity without regard to sex, creed, caste or social status of the parents. Special educational scholarships and facilities must also be provided for women and backward groups and communities.

10.1. *Social security and welfare* : Existing social security schemes such as Employees State Insurance and Provident Fund schemes would be expanded. A scheme for unemployment benefit in the form of paid attendance at training centres with placement facilities would be introduced in urban areas.

10.2. There must be increasing provision for the social welfare of children (foundling homes, crèches, nursery schools, health and recreation centres, etc.), of women (houses for widows, destitute and deserted women; maternity, health, and family planning centres), of juvenile delinquents (remand homes, schools, after-care hostels, etc.), of the handicapped (homes, schools and workshops for the blind, the deaf and the dumb, the crippled, and the mentally deficient or ill, and homes for the aged and the infirm).

11. *Sports and cultural pursuits* : Increasing facilities must be provided for sports and health activities, educational and cultural broadcast and cinema; and the promotion of literature, music, drama, art and other cultural pursuits.

12. *Housing*: Better housing must be provided especially for factory workers and poorer sections of the people in urban areas.

13. *Social overheads* : Expenditure on housing, health, education, social security and welfare, sports and cultural pursuits would necessarily increase purchasing power and create additional demand for consumer goods which must be met by increasing the production of additional consumer goods through household and hand industries in the first instance.

14.1. *Balanced development and controls* : With the stepping up of production of both producer and consumer goods, it would be necessary to provide for adequate increases in the supply of electricity and fuels, irrigation, transport, and communication. Proper balances must be maintained between different sectors so that production is not hampered by bottlenecks.

14.2. The aim of planning would be to avoid shortages giving rise to inflationary pressures on the one hand and over-production with falling prices on the other. In the case of falling prices, especially of consumer goods, the demand would be stimulated promptly by increasing purchasing power through investments in the public sector and through expenditure on social services and by open market operations by Government.

14.3. Government would acquire and keep adequate reserves of foodgrains and important raw materials produced by agriculture to provide against emergencies of short crops in bad years and to maintain prices profitable to peasants in years of exceptionally plentiful crops. This would maintain a minimum level of peasant incomes, stimulate production, and promote the welfare of both peasants and the working class in urban areas.

14.4. Shortages may, however, develop in the short run which would be dealt with as they arise by appropriate methods such as Government intervention in the market, Government trading, physical controls, rationing, and similar measures. Also, the production programme would be adjusted as necessary to restore equilibrium between supply and demand as quickly as possible.

14.5. Rationing of foodgrains, clothing, and similar essential commodities would be avoided. Control over consumption, when necessary, would be related to the shortages of specific physical resources.

15. *Regional development* : Special attention must be given to regional development to reduce disparities in economic opportunities and the level of life between different States.

16.1. *Technical training and scientific research* : A bold plan will require a rapidly increasing technical staff to prepare the various projects as well as to implement them. Training facilities must be expanded sufficiently quickly to turn out technical and scientific personnel in adequate numbers at all levels.

16.2. Scientific and technological research would be expanded and oriented to serve the needs of national development in an effective manner. The National Laboratories, Universities and other scientific institutions and organizations must undertake coordinated researches in accordance with national needs.

16.3. Fundamental research as well as training in research must also be encouraged at the same time to foster the accumulation of basic knowledge and skill for the expansion of applied and technological research.

16.4. The survey of natural resources, especially prospecting for oil and minerals, must be greatly and rapidly increased through State Organizations.

17.1. *Expansion of the public sector* : Key industries would be established and developed in the public sector generally in accordance with the Industrial Policy Resolution of 1948 as interpreted in December 1954. Government would also take up the factory production of certain consumer goods which are of strategic importance for the growth of the national economy.

17.2. The public sector must be expanded rapidly and relatively faster than the private sector for steady advance to a socialistic pattern of economy. In order to make available large capital resources for investment and national development and to facilitate the implementation of the Plan, Government will be prepared to enter into such activities as banking, insurance, foreign trade or trade in selected commodities.

17.3. Government would also promote enterprises in partnership with the private sector so that, although Government would hold a controlling share, initiative can be left to private management subject to policy decisions by Government.

18.1. *The private sector* : A large majority of the population would be engaged in household production in agriculture, in hand industries and in various services which would continue to remain private.

18.2. As the planned demand would have to be matched by the planned production, it would be necessary for the private sector to conform in a general way to the overall programme of production as provided in the Plan. The private sector would be helped by Government by the supply of credit, raw materials, and marketing facilities to undertake production in accordance with the Plan.

18.3. Inducements (such as tax exemption or preferential permission for capital issue) would be given to channel the profits of the private sector into desirable forms of investments in both private and public sectors or in Government bonds and securities.

18.4. The private sector would enjoy the advantages of an assured and growing market in an expanding economy, and thus of reduced risks and uncertainties.

19.1. *Finance and foreign exchange* : Large financial resources would be required for the Second Plan. A small portion would come from sterling balances or foreign loans and aid; and the bulk of the resources must be found from within the domestic economy.

19.2. The tax system would be directed to collect an increasing part of the growing national income in order to permit greater capital formation in the public sector and to finance an expansion of social services.

19.3. The public sector would be extended to industrial and commercial activities where necessary for raising resources for public purposes.

19.4. Deficit financing would be undertaken on the scale necessary to bring about the greatest possible expansion of production

13

without introducing permanent and all-embracing rationing of essential commodities.

19.5. Conspicuous consumption would be discouraged by graduated excise duties; and a more equitable distribution of income would be assured by taxes on property and unearned income.

19.6. Excise duties would be levied to raise additional resources and also to maintain desired price parities between different sectors.

19.7. Steps would be taken to promote exports; and the import of non-essential and luxury goods would be discouraged by heavy duties in order to release foreign exchange resources for more urgent needs.

CHAPTER TWO

TARGETS OF PRODUCTION

1.1. The targets of production (mostly in physical quantities) of some important items are shown in Table (1). The physical unit is given in col. (2) and actual production for 1950-51 and 1953-54 in cols. (3) and (4) respectively. Estimates for 1955-56 and planned target for 1960-61 together with the estimated increase (in percentage) during the plan period are shown in cols. (5), (6) and (7) respectively.

1.2. The above targets are provisional. Estimates of requirements and likely supplies have been examined in a general way on available information. The next task is to carry out a detailed check and make necessary adjustments on the basis of projects to achieve internal consistency in the form of a balanced supply and demand of material and labour resources. Such balancing must also have a proper phasing over time so that neither serious bottlenecks nor excessive supplies emerge at any stage of the Plan.

1.3. Explanatory notes are given on some (but not all) of the items mentioned in Table (1). The number shown within brackets after each item gives the serial number of the same item in Table (1).

2.1. *Electricity* (1) : Planned electrification must be a main link in economic development in India. The hydro-electric projects started in the First Plan must be continued on an increasing scale in the Second Plan.

2.2. Regional grid-systems combining both thermal and hydel power stations must be planned to secure the best use of local fuels (low grade coal, lignite, etc.) and of installed capacity by large consumers (electric-intensive industries like aluminium, alloy-steels etc.) keeping in view the development of a future super-grid for India as a whole.

2.3. Small power stations (hydel and diesel) would also be developed for urgent requirements in small towns and rural areas.

2.4. The use of electricity for small-scale and household industries, irrigation by tube-wells, etc., must be steadily increased.

2.5. The production of electricity must forestall the growth of industrial production; and the installed capacity must increase from 2.8 million kilowatts in 1953-54 to 6 million kilowatts in 1960-61, that is, must be more than doubled. Also, the utilization of capacity must be increased.

3.1. *Coal* (2) : The production of coal must be increased from 37 million tons in 1955-56 to 60 million tons in 1960-61 (an increase of about 62 per cent) which would be difficult to achieve but should not be impossible.

3.2. There is great wastage at present of high grade coking coal of which supply is short. Necessary Government action must be taken without any delay to prevent such wastage and to promote better conservation.

4.1. *Synthetic petrol and products* (3) : India is short of petrol and meets most of its requirements by imports. In addition to increasing oil-prospecting as quickly as possible, a State plant to produce about 300,000 tons of synthetic petrol must be installed during the Second Plan, and future production must be increased as necessary.

4.2. The above plant must also be used to establish a base for the development of associated chemical industries.

5.1. *Steel* (4) : India has vast resources of iron ore; and increasing production of steel must be made an important link in economic development. The installed capacity would be increased to 6 million tons and production to 5 million tons by 1960-61.

5.2. Necessary action (in the way of establishing a heavy machinery industry and promotion of metallurgical research) must be taken in the Second Five Year Plan to build up the base for the future expansion of the installed capacity of steel by at least one million ton per year from 1961.

5.3. Increasing production of steel would supply a secure foundation for the fabrication of plants and machinery of all kinds, expansion of construction work and of railways and transport generally. If necessary, steel can also be exported to neighbouring countries which are in urgent need of it.

6.1. *Aluminium* (7) : India has large reserves of bauxite and the production of aluminium must be rapidly increased to take the place of copper which is in short supply and mostly imported. Increasing production of aluminium would, in its turn, facilitate electrification; and the production of both electricity and aluminium must be continuously increased at the same time.

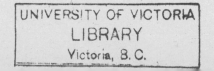

6.2. The production of aluminium should be increased from about 5 to 40 thousand tons during the plan period. One or more aluminium plants must be established in the public sector for this purpose.

7. *Manganese ore* (8) : The extraction of manganese ore must be increased and some of the ore must be converted into ferromanganese before export so as to retain a part of the value created by semi-manufacture.

8. *Cement* (9) : The production of cement must be increased from 4.6 to 10 million tons or more than doubled during the second plan period. The production of other building materials must be increased proportionately to avoid shortages and bottlenecks in construction work.

9.1. *Fertilizers* (10) : The production of nitrogenous fertilizer must be increased by about three times by establishing at least three more factories of roughly the same capacity as Sindri.

9.2. Fertilizer production must also be steadily and continuously expanded along with irrigation to secure a rapid increase in the outturn of agricultural crops in future.

10. *Heavy chemicals* (11) : The production of sulphuric acid, soda ash and caustic soda must be increased by 1960-61 to roughly four times the actual production in 1953-54.

11.1. *Heavy machinery* (12): For rapid industrialization it is essential to fabricate plants and machinery at home. To instal a plant for the production of one million tons of steel per year it is necessary at present to import machinery worth about Rs. 40 or Rs. 45 crores from outside. Provision has been made for investment of Rs. 150 crores to establish large engineering workshops to fabricate machinery needed for producer goods plants. An immediate aim would be to manufacture every year most of the machinery required for installing a one million ton capacity steel plant.

11.2. Investment of Rs. 40 crores is contemplated for establishing plants for the manufacture of heavy electrical equipment.

11.3. The production of machinery for the manufacture of consumer goods (textiles, etc.) must be roughly doubled during the plan period, and an investment provision of Rs. 50 crores has been made for the purpose.

12. *Railway rolling stock* (13) : The annual production of locomotives must be increased from 100 to 400; of wagons from 7,000 to 20,000; and of coaches from 800 to 2,000 so as to attain self-sufficiency in rolling stock by the end of the plan period.

13. *Jute textiles* (14) : Immediate steps should be taken to ensure a fuller use of the existing capacity and to see that by 1960-61
the full rated capacity is utilized.

14.1. *Factory made consumer goods* : The. factory production
of essential consumer goods would be increased in such a way as
to prevent competition with the household and hand industries.

14.2. *Cotton textiles* (15) : Production would be increased to
5,500 million yards per year by 1960-61, the additional production
being used mainly for exports.   (The remaining part of the internal
demand would be met by hand-made cloth).

14.3. *Woollen textiles* (16) : Manufacture of woollen textiles
should increase by about 25 per cent during the second plan
period.

14.4. *Sugar* (17) and *vegetable oil* (18) : The production of
sugar must be increased (preferably through cooperatives) by about
50 per cent and reach 2.1 million tons.   A rise by about 33 per cent
of the production of vegetable oil will be necessary.

14.5. *Paper* (19), *bicycles* (20), *sewing machines* (21), and *electrical
goods* (22) : Production must increase by roughly between 40
per cent and 100 per cent to meet anticipated increase in demand
and also partly for export.

15.1. *Hand-made consumer goods* : Every effort must be made
to expand the hand production of consumer goods to provide a
marketable surplus to meet the increase in demand.

15.2. *Khadi and handloom* (23) : Production would be increased
to 3,200 million yards (from the level of about 1,200 million yards
in 1953-54).

15.3. Production of other hand-made articles must be increased
from 20 per cent to 40 per cent.

16.1. *Agriculture and allied pursuits* : The production of *cereals*
(28) must be increased from 56 million tons in 1953-54 to 63 million
tons in 1960-61, and of *pulses and gram* (29) from 10 to 13 million
tons. This would make the country self-sufficient in foodgrains
at a somewhat higher standard of consumption than at present.

16.2. *Cotton* (32) : Output must increase by 38 per cent to
5.8 million bales so that the net import of cotton can be considerably
reduced by 1960-61.

16.3. *Sugarcane* (34): Output must increase to 7.5 million
tons of raw sugar (50 per cent increase).

16.4. *Milk* (37) : Production of milk and other edible animal
husbandry products should go up by about 25 per cent,

17.1. *Irrigation* (41) : In order to achieve the agricultural targets mentioned above, the total irrigated area must increase from 70 to 100 million acres.

17.2. Special attention must be given to devising suitable measures for flood control.

18. *National extension service and community projects* (42) : Vigorous organization and persistent efforts would be required for the expansion of production in agriculture and in household and hand industries. NES blocks, which can supply a convenient machinery for this purpose, must cover the entire country by the end of the Second Plan.

19. *Transport : Railway tracks* (43) would be increased by 3,000 miles (9 per cent increase); *passenger miles* (44) and *freight ton-miles* (45) by 30 per cent and 40 per cent respectively. *National highways* (46) would be increased from 12,500 to 17,500 miles (40 per cent increase) and *State roads* (47) from 20,000 to 35,000 miles (75 per cent increase). *Shipping tonnage* (48) would increase from 525,000 (in 1953-54) to about 1,500,000, an increase of 185 per cent.

20.1. *Education :* The number of pupils in schools between the ages of 6 and 14 would increase from about 29 million in 1955-56 to about 46 million in 1960-61.

20.2. The expenditure on *technical training, higher education and research* (53) must increase by 75 per cent.

21.1. *Health :* The number of *hospital beds* (54) must increase from 112,000 in 1953-54 to 250,000 in 1960-61; and the number of *registered doctors* (55) from 65,000 in 1953-54 to 90,000 in 1960-61.

21.2. Two new cadres of junior and senior *health assistants* (56) would be created with two levels of training of two years and four years respectively. Each junior health assistant would be placed in charge of a group of 10 villages or one NES block and one senior health assistant would be in charge of 5 such groups or 5 NES blocks together with one registered doctor in charge of two such units or 10 NES blocks in such a way that the whole of the rural area is covered by the end of the Second Plan.

22. *Urban housing* (57) : The number of urban houses must increase sufficiently to provide additional accommodation for 3 million families during the Second Plan.

TABLE (1)   TARGETS OF PRODUCTION FOR THE SECOND FIVE
YEAR PLAN : 1956-57 to 1960-61

name of item	unit	actuals		provisional estimates		
		1950 –51	1953 –54	1955 –56	1960 –61	percentage increase
(1)	(2)	(3)	(4)	(5)	(6)	(7)
factory producer goods						
1. electricity	m. kw	2.3	2.8	3.5	6.0	71
2. coal	m. tons	32	36	37	60	62
3. synthetic petrol	th. tons	nil	nil	nil	300	—
4. steel	m. tons	1.1	1.1	1.3	5.0	285
5. pig iron (for foundries)	m. tons	—	—	0.4	1.8	350
6. iron ore	m. tons	3	4	4	13	225
7. aluminium	th. tons	3.7	3.8	5	40	700
8. manganese ore	m. tons	1	2	2	3.5	75
9. cement	m. tons	2.7	4.0	4.6	10.0	108
10. fertilizers						
(a) nitrogenous	th. tons nitrogen	9.2	61.4	90	360	300
(b) superphosphates	th. tons	55	66	100	200	100
11. heavy chemicals						
(a) sulphuric acid	th. tons	99	120	150	450	200
(b) soda ash	th. tons	45	56	75	200	167
(c) caustic soda	th. tons	11	25	33	100	203
12. heavy machinery to fabricate plants (investment)						
(a) steel and producer goods	Rs. crores	nil	nil	nil	150	—
(b) electrical equipment	Rs. crores	nil	nil	nil	40	—
(c) consumer goods	index	—	—	100	200	100
13. railway rolling stock						
(a) locomotives	no.	nil	86	100	400	300
(b) wagons	no.	1095	6892	7000	20000	186
(c) passenger coaches	no.	479	786	800	2000	150
14. jute textiles	th. tons	892	864	1000	1200	20
factory consumer goods						
15. cotton textiles	m. yds.	3718	4906	5000	5500	10
16. woollen textiles	m. lbs.	18	20	20	25	25
17. sugar	m. tons	1.1	1.1	1.4	2.1	50
18. vegetable oil	m. tons	1.2	1.4	1.5	2.0	33
19. paper	th. tons	114	137	140	200	43
20. bicycles	thousand	101	290	500	1000	100
21. sewing machines	thousand	33	68	90	150	67
22. electrical goods	index	—	—	100	166	66
hand-made consumer goods						
23. khadi and hand-loom	m. yds.	742	1200	1600	3200	100
24. soap	th. tons	—	—	28	40	43
25. foot wear	m. pairs	—	—	80	100	25
26. food industries	index	—	—	100	120	20
27. metalwares	index	—	—	100	133	33
agricultual and associated pursuits						
28. cereals	m. tons	41.7	56.1	56	63	13
29. pulses and grams	m. tons	8.3	9.6	10	13	30
30. total foodgrains	m. tons	50.0	65.0	66	76	15
31. oilseeds	m. tons	5.1	5.6	5.6	7.0	25

TABLE (1) : TARGETS OF PRODUCTION FOR THE SECOND FIVE
YEAR PLAN : 1956-57 TO 1960-61—(*Continued*)

name of item	unit	actuals		provisional estimates		
		1950 –51	1953 –54	1955 –56	1960 –61	percen- tage increase
(1)	(2)	(3)	(4)	(5)	(6)	(7)
32. cotton	.. m. bales	2.9	3.9	4.2	5.8	38
33. jute	.. m. bales	3.3	3.1	5.0	5.4	8
34. sugarcane (raw sugar)	.. m. tons	5.6	4.6	5.0	7.5	50
35. tobacco	.. th. tons	257	256	250	300	20
36. tea	.. m. tons	607	675	675	750	11
37. milk	.. index	—	—	100	125	25
38. wool	.. m. lbs.	—	—	40	50	25
39. timber	.. index	—	—	100	130	30
40. fish	.. ndex	—	—	100	125	25
rural development						
41. irrigation	.. m. acres	50	58	70	100	43
42. NES and community projects	no. of blocks	—	479	1200	5600	367
transport : railways						
43. mileage	.. miles	—	—	34,500	37,500	9
44. passenger miles	.. index	—	—	100	130	30
45. freight ton-miles	.. index	—	—	100	140	40
roads						
46. national highways	.. th. miles	11.9	—	12.5	17.5	40
47. State roads	.. th. miles	17.6	—	20.0	35.0	75
shipping						
48. tonnage	.. thousand	391	525	610	1,500	146
social services ; education						
49. pupils : age 6–11	.. lakh	187	—	236	380	161
50. pupils : age 11–14	.. lakh	34	—	51	80	157
51. percentage of students in age groups : 6–11	.. per cent	42	—	50	75	50
52. ,, ,, 11–14	.. per cent	14	—	20	30	50
53. technical training, higher education and research	index of expenditure	—	—	100	175	75
health						
54. hospital beds	.. thousand	107	112	125	250	100
55. doctors (registered)	thousand	—	65	70	90	29
56. health assistants	.. index	—	—	100	300	200
housing						
57. urban houses	.. lakh	101	—	120	150	25
communication						
58. post offices	.. thousand	37	47	53	78	47
59. telegraph offices	.. thousand	36	39	48	70	46
60. telephones	.. thousand	168	220	300	600	100

14

COMMODITY BALANCES IN 1960-61 (*Provisional*)

1. Attempts have been made to see, in a rough way, that the targets given in Table (1) are consistent. This appendix gives relevant information for five major commodities : electricity, coal, steel, cement, and heavy chemicals.

2. *Electricity :* The consumption of electricity in 1960-61 is expected to be 20,000 million kilowatt hours (kwh) which should be possible to secure from an installed capacity of 6 million kilowatts (mkw) with a slightly higher rate of utilization than the present rate. The following allocation of power in million kwh is envisaged in 1960-61 : iron and steel (2500), aluminium (1300), cement (1100), cotton textiles (1500), fertilizers (1000), all other industries (5600) and light, small power, traction and all other uses (7000)—total (20,000).

3. *Coal :* The industrial development envisaged would require at least 60 million tons of coal. The allocation in million tons in 1960-61 is expected to be as follows : railways (14.0), electricity (5.0), iron and steel (15.0), cement and bricks (5.0), cotton textiles (1.5), jute mills (0.5), paper (1.0), fertilizers (1.0), other industries (4.0), bunker and steamer service (2.0), domestic (7.5), synthetic petrol (1.5), and all other uses (2.0)—total (60.0).

4. *Steel :* The rough pattern of utilization in million tons in 1960-61 is given below : steel processing industries (1.5), railways (0.8), industrial development schemes both public and private (0.8), other Government development schemes including multipurpose and State irrigation projects (0.2), construction (0.5), industrial maintenance and packing (0.3), defence and roads (0.1), and all other uses including export (0.7)—total (5.0).

5. *Cement :* The allocation envisaged in million tons in 1960-61 is as follows : all construction (6.4), cement products (0.4), railways (0.5), roads (0.3), multipurpose and State irrigation projects (1.8), and all other uses including export (0.6)—total (10.0).

6.1. *Heavy chemicals :* Balances have been worked out for sulphuric acid, caustic soda and soda ash.

6.2. *Sulphuric acid :* The allocation in 1960-61 in thousand tons will be as follows : ammonium sulphate (60), superphosphate (110), iron and steel (90) and all other uses (190)—total (450).

6.3. *Caustic soda :* The allocation in 1960-61 in thousand tons will be as follows : soap (30), textiles (20), paper (15), aluminium (5) and all other uses (30)—total (100).

6.4. *Soda ash :* The allocation in 1960-61 in thousand tons will be as follows : glass (100), textiles (10), silicate of soda (10), paper (10), other chemicals (25) and all other uses (45)—total (200).

CHAPTER THREE

INVESTMENT AND DEVELOPMENT

1.1. *Allocation of investment :* The allocation of investment (or net capital formation) by broad sectors is shown in Table (2).

TABLE (2) : ALLOCATION OF INVESTMENT
(Rs. crores)

sector	public	private	total	percentage
(1)	(2)	(3)	(4)	(5)
1. electricity	450	50	500	8.9
2. industry	1,000	400	1,400	25.0
3. transport & communication	850	50	900	16.1
4. agriculture & irrigation	750	200	950	17.1
5. construction	250	1,100	1,350	24.0
6. stocks	100	400	500	8.9
total	3,400	2,200	5,600	100.0

1.2. Electricity includes both hydro-electric and thermal power stations. Industry includes the household and hand industries. Construction includes residential houses, schools, hospitals, and public buildings.

1.3. Strictly comparable figures are not available for the First Five Year Plan, but the total investment in the public sector as planned was roughly Rs. 1600 to 1700 crores and the same amount was estimated for the private sector. Thus investment or net capital formation through the public sector in the Second Plan would be about double of the planned estimates in the First Plan; and the estimated investment in the private sector would be about 40 per cent higher.

2.1. *Allocation by industries :* The breakdown of investment by important industries is shown in Table (3).

2.2. The provision for iron and steel includes expansion of capacity of existing plants; three new plants (Rourkela, Madhya Pradesh and one more); factories for the production of pig iron for foundries, and miscellaneous items.

2.3.   Along with the installation of one synthetic petrol plant, necessary action must be taken to train personnel and build up experience through pilot plants for the establishment of associated chemical industries.

2.4.   The production of electrical appliances would include electrical machinery (such as turbines, generators, transformers, transmission equipment etc.) required for hydro-electric and thermal projects.

2.5.   The heavy machinery industry to be established in the public sector must be able by 1960-61 to fabricate machinery required to instal every year a steel plant of a million ton capacity or plants to manufacture producer goods of roughly equivalent value.

TABLE (3) :   ALLOCATION OF INVESTMENT BY INDUSTRIES

industry	investment (Rs. crores)	percentage
(1)	(2)	(3)
1. iron and steel	425	30.4
2. synthetic petrol	80	5.7
3. heavy machinery to fabricate plants for		
(a) steel and producer goods	150	10.7
(b) electrical equipment	40	2.9
(c) consumer goods	50	3.6
4. cement, chemicals, etc.	100	7.1
5. existing State enterprises	50	3.6
6. aluminium	30	2.1
7. minerals and prospecting	75	5.4
8. fertilizers	100	7.1
9. factory consumer goods	100	7.1
10. household and hand industries	200	14.3
total	1,400	100.0

2.6.   The aluminium industry must be developed to make the country independent of imports of copper by 1960-61; and must continue to be further expanded in future.

2.7.   Geological surveys and especially prospecting for oil and minerals by Government organization must be rapidly expanded. Mining operations must also be greatly expanded. A provision of Rs. 75 crores has been made for this purpose.

2.8.   Rs. 100 crores have been provided for the installation of fertilizer plants with capacity equivalent to roughly four times the current production at the Sindri factory.

2.9.   The greatest importance is attached to the expansion of the household and hand industries as this would be the principal method of liquidating unemployment and also of creating a marketable surplus of consumer goods to meet the increase in demand arising from investments in heavy industries, construction work, and expenditure on social services.   Rs. 200 crores or Rs. 40 crores per year have been provided for this purpose.

3.1.   *Public development expenditure :*   In the First as well as in the Second Plan certain items of current expenditure have been included in addition to provision for investment.   This is shown in Table (4).

TABLE (4) :   PUBLIC DEVELOPMENT EXPENDITURE

sector	second plan				first plan	
	invest-ment (Rs. crores)	current (Rs. crores)	total (Rs. crores)	per cent	per cent	total (Rs. crores)
(1)	(2)	(3)	(4)	(5)	(6)	(7)
1. electricity	450	—	450	10.5		
2. agriculture, irrigation and rural development	750	200	950	22.5		
sub-total			(1,400)	(33)	44	990
3. industry & minerals	1,000	100	1,100	26	8	178
4. transport and communication	850	100	950	22	24	536
5. construction and social services	250	500	750	17	24	544
6. stocks	100	—	100	2	—	—
total	3,400	900	4,300	100	100	2,248

3.2.   Comparable figures for the First Five Year Plan are given in cols. (6) and (7).   The total development expenditure of Rs. 4,300 crores in the Second Plan is just short of double the planned development expenditure of Rs. 2,248 crores in   the   First Plan.

3.3.   In the Second Plan there is a much larger actual expenditure for industrial and mineral development (Rs. 1,100 crores against Rs. 178 crores in the First Plan); and the relative proportion is also much higher (26 per cent of total development expenditure in the Second Plan against 8 per cent in the First Plan).   The actual expenditure in the Second Plan is greater but the relative expenditure (as a proportion of the total) is less in all the other sectors.

4.1. *Total development expenditure :* In addition to the current development expenditure included in Table (4), there are current expenditures for purposes of development not included in the Plan. The position is shown in Table (5) below.

TABLE (5) : TOTAL GOVERNMENT EXPENDITURE
(Rs. crores)

item	1955-56 (estimated)	1960-61 (estimated)	total second plan
(1)	(2)	(3)	(4)
1. non-development (defence and civil administration)	625	725	3,400
2. development			
(a) not in the plan	200	225	1,100
(b) in the plan	600	1,100	4,300
3. sub-total	800	1,325	5,400
total	1,425	2,050	8,800

4.2. The total Government expenditure is expected to increase from Rs. 1,425 crores in 1955-56 to about Rs. 2,050 crores in 1960-61 the total development expenditure would increase at the same time from Rs. 800 crores to Rs. 1,325 crores; and the development expenditure included in the Second Five Year Plan would increase from Rs. 600 crores to Rs. 1,100 crores.

4.3. The total Government expenditure during the Second Five Year Plan is expected to be Rs. 8,800 crores out of which Rs. 3,400 crores would be non-development (defence and civil administration), Rs. 1,100 crores development expenditure not included in the Plan, and Rs. 4,300 crores development expenditure included in the Plan.

CHAPTER FOUR

EMPLOYMENT AND INCOME

1.1. *Employment* : In India a very large number of families (comprising a majority of the population) are self-employed, many of which use their labour power only partially and thus suffer from chronic under employment. They must be provided with opportunities of doing more work and thus increasing their income.

1.2. In the urban areas there is a large number of persons without jobs and seeking work for whom new employment must be created. New work must also be found for roughly 1.8 million persons who, on an average, would enter the working force every year (calculated on the basis of a labour force composition of 40 per cent of a net average increase in population of 4.5 million per year.

2.1. The programme of production, investment, and development (discussed in Chapters Two and Three) is expected to generate a volume of employment shown in Table (6).

TABLE (6) : ESTIMATED VOLUME OF EMPLOYMENT IN 1960-61

sector	employment (in million)		increase	
	1955-56	1960-61	actual (million)	per cent
(1)	(2)	(3)	(4)	(5)
1. agriculture & allied pursuits	109.5	111.0	1.5	1.4
2. mining & factory establishments	4.0	5.7	1.7	42
3. household enterprises & construction	12.0	15.0	3.0	25
4. communication, railways, banks, insurance	1.6	2.0	0.4	25
5. wholesale and retail trade, transport (other than railways), etc.	10.0	12.0	2.0	20
6. professions, services (including govt. administration) and the rest	14.9	17.3	2.4	16
total	152.0	163.0	11.0	7

2.2. If the targets of production are realized then the problem of unemployment should be brought under control by the end of the Second Five Year Plan. Because of the rapid rate of industrialization, proportionately the biggest increase of employment, about 45 per cent, would occur in mining and factory enterprises. The household and hand industries, communication, transport, trade, etc., would have an increase of about 20 per cent or 25 per cent and the professions and services of about 16 per cent. Even in the Second Plan labour would not begin to be drawn away from agriculture and allied pursuits, but would increase at a low rate of the order of only 1.5 per cent, which would still mean an increase of 1.5 million persons in the labour force in this sector.

3.1. *Income :* The net domestic output at 1952-53 prices had increased from Rs. 91.9 abja in 1950-51 (the base year of the First Five Year Plan) to about Rs. 103.1 abja (provisional estimate) in 1953-54. This represents an increase of Rs. 11.2 abja or 12.2 per cent in 4 years or just over 3 per cent per year. A part of this increase was probably due to exceptionally good agricultural crops in 1953-54 and another part possibly to a partial correction of the previous underestimation of crops. If allowance is made for these factors the real increase would be probably about 10 per cent in 4 years.

3.2. In the Second Five Year Plan the rate of investment and development would be roughly double that of the First Plan. The rate of increase of income is also expected to be roughly double or about 5 per cent per year. The same estimate has been generally corroborated from more detailed calculations by sectors on the basis of the investment and development programme.

3.3. The expected increase in national income is shown in Table (7).

TABLE (7) : DOMESTIC PRODUCT OF THE INDIAN UNION
AT 1952-53 PRICES

Rs. abja (= 100 crores)

sector	(actual) 1950-51	(estimated)		increase per cent
		1955-56	1960-61	
(1)	(2)	(3)	(4)	(5)
1. agriculture and allied pursuits	45.2	52.8	63.4	20
2. mining and factory enterprises	6.6	9.0	15.0	67
3. household enterprises & construction	9.3	10.2	14.3	40
4. communication, railways, banks, etc.	3.1	3.6	4.7	30
5. wholesale & retail trade, other transport	13.4	15.1	18.8	25
6. professions, services including govt. administration and the rest	14.3	17.3	20.8	20
7. total	91.9	108.0	137.0	27
8. population (million)	359.3	383.7	409.7	7
9. per capita income (Rs.)	256	282	334	19

15

Chapter Five

FINANCE AND FOREIGN EXCHANGE

1. *Rate of investment :* The planned net investment covering both public and private sectors is Rs. 5,600 crores over the period of the Second Plan. The current rate of investment is about 7 per cent; this will have to be raised to about 11 per cent of national income by 1960-61.

2.1. *Resources for the public sector :* The total expenditure of the Centre and State Governments combined is estimated at Rs. 8,800 crores for the Second Plan as a whole (Table 5). Expenditure outside the plan would increase from Rs. 825 crores in 1955-56 (estimated) to Rs. 900 crores on an average in the Second Plan. Expenditure on the Plan is expected to increase from Rs. 600 crores in 1955-56 (estimated) to an average of Rs. 860 crores in the Second Plan.

2.2. The total receipts from taxes and non-tax revenue, at the current rate of intake of 8.5 per cent of national income, would bring in about Rs. 5,200 crores. Borrowings (net) from the public should yield Rs. 1,000 crores (about Rs. 600 crores from loans and Rs. 400 crores from small savings). Allowing for Rs. 200 crores for receipts from railways and miscellaneous items on capital account, the total receipts from domestic sources, at current rates, would be Rs. 6,400 crores.

2.3. This leaves a gap of Rs. 2,400 crores in the public sector. As against this, external assistance may provide Rs. 400 crores. The balance of Rs. 2,000 crores will have to be found at least in part by fresh taxation and profits of such commercial or industrial undertakings as can be started in the public sector. The aim should be to limit deficit financing to a total of Rs. 1,000 to 1,200 crores. A taxation target of 9 to 10 per cent of national income as against the present level of about 7 per cent must be attained.

3.1. The budgetary position on the above basis is shown in Table (8).

3.2. A good part of the additional income in the Second Plan would be created at lower income levels. The heavy industries would take time to become profitable. Also, foreign assistance may not be realised to the fullest extent. It would be essential, therefore, to keep a stringent watch on expenditure outside the Plan, to make necessary adjustments in the price and subsidy policy of Government, to reach new strata for tapping savings, and finally, to make changes in the tax structure to raise additional resources required to finance the Second Plan.

TABLE (8) :   GOVERNMENT BUDGET : 1956-57 TO 1960-61
(Rs. crores)

expenditure		receipts	
(1)	(2)	(3)	(4)
1. on the plan	4,300	1. on the revenue account	5,200
2. outside the plan	4,500	2. loans from the public	1,000
		3. railways and miscellaneous funds	200
		4. foreign assistance	400
		5. sub-total	6,800
		6. additional taxes and loans and profits from State enterprises	800–1,000
		7. deficit financing	1,000–1,200
total	8,800	total	8,800

4.1.   *Finance of the private sector :*   Investment in the private sector is estimated at Rs. 2,200 crores out of which Rs. 1,100 crores or about a half is for housing and Rs. 400 crores for industries.

4.2.   With deficit financing of Rs. 1,000 to Rs. 1,200 crores by Government, the banking system should be able to provide the credit required for working capital. In fact, conditions of easy credit are likely to emerge.

4.3.   The newly set-up financial institutions (such as the Industrial Investment and Credit Corporation) will assist the private sector. The pattern of investment in the private sector will have to be watched continuously and influenced in the desired direction through tax incentives, selective credit controls, capital issue control and similar devices.

5.1.   *Foreign trade and payments :*   Much larger import will have to be made of capital goods in the Second Plan. The total need would come to about Rs. 1,200 crores; adding Rs. 400 crores for import of equipment for replacements, the total requirement would be about Rs. 1,600 crores for import of capital goods.

5.2.   This must be met partly by increased production of foodgrains, sugar, cotton, and petrol; partly through foreign assistance and withdrawal from sterling balances; and by curtailment of non-essential imports and promotion of exports in every possible way.

CHAPTER SIX

PLANNING ORGANIZATION AND ADMINISTRATION

1.1. *Planning organization :* Planning must be continuous and flexible. In addition to the Five Year Plan, detailed annual plans must be prepared every year. Targets, projects, and policies must be continually reassessed and reformulated to suit changing needs and conditions.

1.2. At the same time it is imperative to keep in perspective the potential growth of the economy over a long period so that decisions can be made to secure a balance between short term and long term objectives.

1.3. For planning on lines explained above, it is necessary to build up an appropriate planning organization. A technical organization (consisting of economists, statisticians, scientists, engineers, technologists, and administrators) must be established within the Planning Commission for the preparation and continuing examination of the national plan and for working out the various balances relating to it. Technical units must also be established in the Central Ministries, State Governments, and other agencies to prepare detailed projects and estimates and to revise them as necessary.

1.4. There must be a continual two-way flow of information. Plan targets from the top must be continually checked against possibilities of realization at the level of projects. Possibilities of development envisaged at the bottom must continuously shape the targets formulated at the top.

1.5. Information of many kinds would be continually required for the formulation and revision of the plan and of detailed projects as well as for the assessment of the progress and implementation of the Plan.

1.6. The information service and planning and project activities must be closely related. The Central Statistical Organization in association with the Indian Statistical Institute must function as an integral part of the planning machinery at the Centre. Following the same pattern, the State Statistical Bureaus must serve as focal points for statistical services in connection with planning activities at the State level.

2.1. *Administrative machinery :* Planning on bold lines with a steady expansion of the public sector and advance to a socialistic pattern of economy would require the building up of appropriate administrative machinery of a new type at all levels.

2.2. There must be decentralization, on business-like lines, of the day to day management of public enterprises with large delegation of financial, administrative, and executive control to develop initiative and responsibility at the periphery so necessary for efficient conduct of business enterprises.

2.3. Attention must be focussed on the implementation of the Plan—on getting things done at the right time—and rules of procedure must, if necessary, be revised to ensure effective action. Secretariat control of the present type must be replaced to a large extent by control, by truly autonomous public corporations set up by Government or through the supply of credit by State Banks working under the general guidance of Government in matters of policy.

2.4. Administrative difficulties inherent in the existing Government machinery are likely to prove the greatest obstacle to efficient planning. To overcome such difficulties, large organizational and even constitutional changes may become necessary. The problem is urgent and requires immediate and serious attention.

2.5. Government must rally public support in favour of the Plan and encourage and help non official organizations to promote its fulfilment.

EXTRACTS FROM THE SECOND FIVE YEAR PLAN
A TENTATIVE FRAME-WORK

Working paper prepared jointly by the Economic Division, Ministry of Finance and the Economic Division, Planning Commission in consultation with the Central Statistical Organization and the Indian Statistical Institute.

CHAPTER ONE

OBJECTIVES OF THE SECOND PLAN

*　　　*　　　*　　　*　　　*　　　*

NATIONAL INCOME AND STANDARD OF LIVING

5†.　The First Five Year Plan contained an illustrative model of development over a period of some 27 years. According to that model, India's national income could be doubled in some 22 years, per capita income could be doubled in about 27 years, and per capita consumption could be increased by roughly 70 per cent in a little more than five plan periods (i.e., between 1950-51- and 1977).

6.　The increase in national income by the end of the First Plan is likely to be greater than was anticipated and may amount to some 15 per cent over the five years. The national income of India increased by some 15 per cent in real terms during the five years 1948-49 to 1953-54. During the first three years of the First Plan, the increase was of the order of 12.5 per cent. Even when allowance is made for the provisional character of the estimate for 1953-54 and for favourable monsoons, it is reasonable to expect a 15 per cent increase in national income over the First Plan period. For the Second Plan, therefore, we may well aspire to an increase in national income higher than 15 per cent say, 25 to 27 per cent in five years, or 5 per cent per annum as a first approximation.

7.　An increase in national income of about 5 per cent every year in the Second Plan is by no means unrealistic or ambitious.

---

† Original numbering of paragraphs has been retained,

A rate of increase in national income of 3 per cent per annum has been achieved over a period of years without any attempt at planning in countries already advanced industrially. In recent years, the socialist countries in Eastern Europe have achieved a rate of increase of some 12 to 16 per cent in national income every year. In the light of this experience, the target of a 5 per cent per annum increase in national income for the Second Five Year Plan must be regarded as a minimum to aim at. With effort and organization, it should probably be improved upon. On this basis, it should be possible to advance the long-term targets outlined in the First Plan by some four to five years, or even more.

NET NATIONAL OUTPUT OF INDIA AT CURRENT AND CONSTANT PRICES

(1)	*1953–54 (2)	1952–53 (3)	1951–52 (4)	1950–51 (5)	1949–50 (6)	1948.49 (7)
net output in Rs. abja**						
at current prices	106.0	98.6	99.9	95.3	90.1	86.5
at 1948-49 prices	99.5	95.2	91.6	88.5	88.2	86.5
per capita net output in Rs.						
at current prices	283.9	267.4	274.5	265.2	253.9	246.9
at 1948-49 prices	266.5	258.1	251.7	246.3	248.6	246.9
index number of net output with 1948-49 as base						
at current prices	122.5	114.0	115.5	110.2	104.2	100.0
at 1948-49 prices	115.0	110.1	105.9	102.2	102.0	10.00
index number of per capita net output with 1948-49 as base						
at current prices	115.0	108.3	111.2	107.4	102.8	100.0
at 1948-49 prices	107.9	104.5	101.9	99.8	100.7	100.0

* preliminary.   ** abja = 100 crores = 10^9

8.   An increase in national income of some five per cent per annum would permit both a sizable improvement in the level of living in the country and an increase in the rate of investment. If investment is stepped up from roughly 7 per cent of national income at present to about 11 per cent of national income by the end of the Second Plan, total consumption should increase roughly by 20 per cent and per capita consumption by 12 to 13 per cent by the end of the Second Plan.

GROWTH IN NATIONAL INCOME IN SELECTED COUNTRIES

country	period	rate of growth (annual average in per cent)
(1)	(2)	(3)
U. S. A.	1869-78-1904-13	4.5
	1869-78-1929	4.0
	1899-1908-1929	3.2
	1929-1950	3.0
Canada	1903-29	2.6
Switzerland	1890-1929	2.7
Germany	1876-1913	2.8
Japan	1887-1913	3.0
	1914-1930	6.7
	1914-1937	6.7
Australia	1901-03-1928-29	3.2
	1901-03-1947-48	2.5
Soviet Union	1928-37 (official)	16
	1949-53 ,,	15
Poland	1947-53 ,,	14.5
Czechoslovakia	1948-53 ,,	12
Hungary	1952-53 ,,	12
Bulgaria	1952-53 ,,	16

9. The First Five Year Plan aimed, as a first step, at restoring the pre-war levels of consumption of the basic necessaries of life in the country. There has been a significant increase in the consumption of foodgrains, cloth and other items in recent years and the damage done by war and partition is all but repaired. However, the standards of nutrition, clothing, health, housing and education in the country are still inadequate.

10. The minimum requirements of cereals in a balanced diet were estimated by the Nutrition Advisory Committee as 14 oz. per adult per day. The average consumption of cereals in the country has increased from less than 13 oz. per adult per day in 1950-51 to nearly 15 oz. in 1953-54. The availability of pulses and grams still falls short of minimum nutritional requirements—2.5 against 3 oz. per adult per day. The consumption of a large number of people, however, is below the average level in the country; and the demand for foodgrains is certain to increase if purchasing power is increased at the lower levels. Thus, quite apart from the requirements of a growing population, the production of foodgrains needs to be increased in the Second Plan.

11. In the case of other foods such as milk, ghee, meat, fish, eggs, fats, fruits, vegetables and sugar the present level of

consumption falls far short of minimum requirements. In planning for a higher standard of living special attention must be devoted in the Second Plan to animal husbandry, fisheries, poultry-farming, vegetable gardening and other branches of food production. How much advance in these directions can be secured within the next five years is a matter for detailed examination.

12. The average consumption of cotton cloth in India is now back to the pre-war standard of 15 yards per person per year. The Textile Enquiry Committee has recommended an increase in consumption of cotton cloth to 18 yards per person by 1960. This modest objective must be achieved in the Second Plan.

13. During the war, an acute housing shortage developed in the urban areas. Urban population increased by 42 per cent during 1941-1951, and the shortage of houses at the end of the decade was estimated at more than 18 lakhs in addition to some 10 lakh houses required for displaced persons from Pakistan. There has been a substantial increase in urban construction in recent years, and it is reasonable to expect that the supply of houses in the urban areas would increase from some 102 lakhs in 1950-51 to about 115 to 120 lakhs by the end of the First Plan. Broadly, provision has to be made in the Second Plan for the construcion of an additional 30 lakhs of houses in the urban areas. The housing problem in rural areas is not as acute as in urban areas. But an effort must be made through the National Extension Service and similar agencies to improve housing conditions in rural areas as well.

14. As regards education, of the total population of children between 6 and 14, only 23 per cent went to school in 1939-40 and some 32 per cent in 1950-51. It is expected that this proportion would increase to 40 per cent by the end of the First Plan. Under the directive principles of the Constitution, the State must endeavour to provide free and compulsory education to all children below the age of 14 within a period of ten years. A considerable expansion to a proportion of say, 60 per cent, in primary education facilities must, therefore, be achieved in the Second Plan. Similarly, the provision of hospitals, doctors, nurses and sanitation facilities in the country is far from adequate and a substantial increase in health and medical facilities during the Second Plan must be assured.

15. An increase in national product by some 25 per cent would be required to ensure the increase in the level of living as envisaged above.

*   *   *   *

16

SOCIAL JUSTICE

40. As in the case of all things that really matter in life, social justice is easy to recognise but not so easy to define. Since the goal of a socialist pattern has now been clearly accepted, concrete steps in this direction have to be taken during the next plan period.

41. An important element in this transformation must be land reform with a ceiling on holdings and an explicit transfer of property rights to the actual tillers of the soil. In order to be economically meaningful, land reform must be supplemented by consolidation of holdings and by provision of credit, marketing and warehousing facilities in the rural areas on the lines indicated in the report of the Rural Credit Survey.

42. A socialistic pattern of society also implies State ownership or control of the strategic means of production. With the rapid development of basic industries, largely in the public sector, the Second Plan would ensure for the State a significant increase in its influence on this sector. Where necessary, the State must be prepared to enter into other spheres such as banking, insurance and trading.

43. Certain basic necessities of life must be provided to a greater proportion of the people irrespective of their ability to purchase the same in order to achieve a greater equality of opportunities in the country. Among these education and health come first. What is important is not merely an increase of schools and colleges but also an assurance of access to them for children of the poorest parents. The Second Plan must pay special attention to the provision of free boarding, lodging and tuition facilities to poor and deserving students from the primary right up to post-graduate levels. In other words, the sphere of public or communal consumption must be increased as the share of the public sector in productive enterprises goes up.

44. Conspicuous consumption by the more well-to-do classes must be checked. In a poor country trying to lift itself by the bootstraps, the self-denial and labour of the poor must provide directly or indirectly the major part of the resources for development. But such self-denial and effort cannot be justified in the midst of glaring inequalities. Conspicuous consumption by a few persons also serves to dissipate the habit of thrift in others who follow suit in some measure for reasons of social prestige. Curbing of

conspicuous consumption requires a fairly stiff system of taxes on luxuries. But, basically, the solution is reducing expendable incomes through direct taxation.

45. The Taxation Enquiry Commission has recommended that there should be a ceiling on net personal incomes after tax which, generally speaking, should not exceed approximately 30 times the prevailing average per family in the country. This recommendation is intended to be implemented by steps over a period of time; but a few steps must be taken in this direction in the Second Plan.

46. The emphasis on employment opportunities in the Second Plan will raise incomes at lower levels. At the same time, an inflationary rise in prices which corrodes living standards of the workers and the middle class must be avoided as far as possible; and in the event of inflationary measures gathering strength, steps must be taken to prevent the concentration of wealth and incomes in the hands of the trading and profit-making classes.

47. Industrial relations must be so arranged as to provide labour with both economic security and fair wages. The claims of capital accumulation must, of course, have precedence in the allocation of profits but a proportion should be devoted to increasing amenities like housing, providing training with a view to promotion, etc. In public undertakings, the State must set an example as a model employer.

48. Agricultural prices are not likely to remain depressed during a bold plan for rapid industrialisation. In the event of a sustained fall in agricultural prices, demand must be stimulated promptly by greater public expenditure and by open market operations by Government. Any sharp turn in the terms of trade against agriculture would depress the living standards of the large mass of people, jeopardise the increase in agricultural productivity and would curtail demand in general.

CHAPTER TWO

THE SECOND FIVE YEAR PLAN IN OUTLINE

*   *   *   *   *   *   *

II. INVESTMENT AND PRIORITIES IN THE PLAN

31. *** The concept of "investment" bristles with ambiguities; and in view of the variety of concepts in the field, it is necessary to specify clearly what is included in investment here.

32. In the First Five Year Plan, two concepts were used to denote the size of the Plan, *viz.*, net investment and developmental expenditure. Thus the net investment in the public sector was expected to be of the order of Rs. 1,600 to Rs. 1,700 crores; whereas the developmental expenditure which includes outlay of a capital as well as current expenditure was initially estimated at Rs. 2,069 crores. Since outlay on the Plan included only a portion of the outlay on certain developmental heads such as health and education, an additional concept of total developmental outlay (as distinguished from that included in the Plan) has also been used at times to indicate the size of the Plan. In the case of 42 organized industries in private and public sectors, the First Plan considered the requirements of gross rather than net investment in as much as allowance was made for part of depreciation, replacement and modernization. Similarly, the requirements of working capital were taken account of in the case of industries, but not for other sectors.

33. For the purposes of this paper, we speak of 'net investment' when referring to the economy as a whole. If our idea in assessing the 'investment cost' of a plan of certain size and character is to measure the effort of saving that is involved, it is more logical to consider gross income and gross investment. The entire gross product of the economy is, strictly speaking, available for consumption or investment. The allowance to be made for depreciation is in many cases national in the sense that except in the case of repairs maintenance or replacements of real resources are in fact required currently against the estimated amount of depreciation. Replacement itself is seldom a mere substitution of one machine or building

by another of the same type. Nonetheless, since our national income statistics are expressed in net output terms, it may be convenient to relate them to net investment.

34. Non-monetized investment is not included in investment. In a predominantly rural community of self-supporting persons, a significant amount of investment must be done by the application of personal labour and by using locally available materials. With the efforts to mobilise voluntary labour for various nation-building activities such as flood-control, investment in non-money terms must play an important part. It is also illogical not to include such investment when the income generating from it is included in national output. However, in view of the highly conjectural nature of the imputed value of such investment, it is proposed to disregard it at this stage.

35. As regards investment in working capital, *i.e.*, in stocks of goods and services waiting to be consumed or to be utilised in production, it is clear that any additional requirements here are indistinguishable from the requirements of the fixed capital. Both require "savings" in real and financial terms; and as the Rural Credit Survey amply points out, provision of short-term capital has as much relevance to production as that of long-term capital. Indeed unless increments in stocks of *all* goods are included in investment, it would be difficult to justify the inclusion of residential houses in investment. Construction of a house is investment not because it resembles a producer good more than a consumer good but because it represents a net addition to the stock of houses. The requirements of additional working capital over a period are not easy to estimate; but a rough allowance is made for them here.

36. Although it is more meaningful to speak of net investment when referring to the economy as a whole, it is useful to retain the concept of developmental expenditure in speaking of the public sector. Whether this developmental expenditure under the Plan should include only a part or whole of the expenditure in certain specified heads is a question to which we return later. But at this stage, it may be emphasized that as long as we use more than one concept to indicate the size of the Plan in the public sector, it would be essential to recast Government budgets in a manner which would make explicit the magnitudes of all these concepts. Thus, net capital formation through the budget, total developmental outlay and the outlay on the Plan must be all readily ascertainable from the budget statements.

37. The total amount of net investments required for achieving the targets outlined above may be estimated at about Rs. 5,600 crores. This estimate is made up by aggregating, wherever possible, the capital requirements of the individual targets. However, this procedure cannot be adopted uniformly for two reasons. The targets do not cover all the items of production. And in several important sectors, particularly in agriculture, investment is multi-purpose in the sense that only a complex of products can be related to a complex of investment.

38. Again, it is not as if all the investment in the community is strictly required for the achievement of the targets set. Residential construction, stock piling and investment in gold and precious metals can take place irrespective of the requirements of the targets sought to be achieved. It is as well, therefore, to be clear in our minds as to how much allowance we make for such investment.

*   *   *   *   *   *

III. NATIONAL INCOME AND THE STRUCTURE OF THE ECONOMY

48. One way of describing the objectives of the next Plan would be to compare the structure of production as it is expected to emerge at the end of the Plan (1960-61) with that prevailing on the eve of the Plan (1955-56). This is done in the present section.

49. The latest available estimate of India's national income relates to the year 1953-54. At current prices, the national income of India in 1953-54 was approximately Rs. 10,600 crores. In order to present a picture of the change in the economy over the Second Five Year Plan, it is necessary to have an estimate of national income for the year 1955-56. Even if we make allowance for the fact that national income in 1953-54 was somewhat unusually high on account of favourable monsoons, it is not unreasonable to expect that national income over the last two years of the First Plan would increase by some 4 per cent. On this basis, national income in 1955-56 should exceed Rs. 11,000 crores at 1953-54 prices.

50. However, judged by recent trends, prices in 1953-54 were also high. In outlining the change in the economic structure over the Second Plan, we have necessarily to make all calculations at some constant prices. In one sense, it does not matter what particular prices we use. Nonetheless, since some estimates such as those of Government receipts and expenditure are necessarily made at current prices, it is important that other calculations are also made at prices as near as possible to the prices current in the period

under consideration. For the Second Plan, we have worked out our terms of 1952-53 prices in as much as they are nearer to current prices than those in any other recent year for which national income data are available.

INDEX OF WHOLESALE PRICES IN INDIA

(Year ended August 1939 = 100)

year	food articles	industrial raw materials	semi-manufac-tures	manufac-tures	general index
(1)	(2)	(3)	(4)	(5)	(6)
1948-49	383	445	327	346	376
1949-50	391	472	332	347	385
1950-51	416	523	349	354	410
1951-52	399	592	374	401	435
1952-53	358	437	344	371	381
1953-54	384	467	359	367	398
1955, Jan. 22	309	431	345	377	364

51. The national income of India in 1955-56 (at 1952-53 prices) may be estimated at Rs. 10,800 crores. With a 5 per cent increase per annum it should amount to Rs. 13,700 crores in 1960-61—*i.e.*, an increase of Rs. 2,900 crores. This increase is consistent with the targets set as supplemented by assumptions about minor sectors not included in the targets.

52. The increase in national income would not be uniform for different sectors. The table following illustrates the change in the economic structure envisaged for the Second Plan in terms of the sectorwise breakdown employed in national income statistics.

53. It is clear from the table that of the total increase in national income (Rs. 2,900 crores) the largest part would still be in agriculture and allied pursuits (Rs. 1,060 crores). Factory establishments would show an increase in net output of some Rs. 550 crores, mines of Rs. 50 crores and small enterprises of Rs. 410 crores. The rest of the additional output of about Rs. 830 crores would be generated in the tertiary sector. However, in relative terms, the increase in income generated would be greater in factory establishments (65 per cent), mining (50 per cent), and small enterprises (40 per cent) than in agriculture (20 per cent) or in the tertiary sector (23 per cent). On balance, the relative share of mines, factories and small enterprises in the national income would increase from 17.7 per cent in 1955-56 to 21.4 per cent in

1960-61 and that of agriculture would decline correspondingly
from 48.9 per cent to 46.3 per cent. Thus, despite the relatively
high targets for industries, the structure of the economy would
show only a small change over the Second Plan period.

DOMESTIC PRODUCT OF INDIA

(at 1952-53 prices)

sector	products (Rs. abja)			per cent of total product		
	1950-51	1955-56	1960-61	1950-51	1955-56	1960-61
(1)	(2)	(3)	(4)	(5)	(6)	(7)
I. agriculture & allied pursuits	45.2	52.8	63.4	49.2	48.9	46.3
II. mining	0.8	1.0	1.5	0.9	0.9	1.1
III. factory establishments	5.8	8.0	13.5	6.3	7.4	9.9
IV. small enterprises	9.3	10.2	14.3	10.1	9.4	10.4
V. railways, communications, banks, etc.	3.1	3.6	4.7	3.4	3.3	3.4
VI. other commerce and transport	13.4	15.1	18.8	14.6	14.0	13.7
VII. professions, government services, etc.	14.3	17.3	20.8	15.6	16.0	15.2
total product	91.9	108.0	137.0	100.0	100.0	100.0
per capita products (Rs.)	256	282	334	—	—	—

54. The classification of domestic product by sectors given above
does not reveal certain features of the development envisaged for
the Second Plan. Thus, the development of heavy industries is
obscured in the total of factory establishments. Similarly, the small
enterprises sector is not identical with the small industries sector.
It includes in addition workers employed in construction industries. A further breakdown of these sectors can be attempted only
on rough lines. Thus, although the net output of factory establishments increases by two-thirds, the output of consumer goods industries is expected to increase by some 20 per cent only whereas that
of producer goods by 150 to 175 per cent. In the case of small
enterprises, as against a total increase of 40 per cent in net output,
that of consumer goods is envisaged to increase by one-third,
of producer goods by 50 per cent and of construction enterprises
by some 60 per cent.

55. Similarly, the increase in agricultural output of 20 per cent
comprises a 15 per cent increase in foodgrains and 25 per cent in
other foodstuffs and commercial crops.

56. In short, the structure of production envisaged here is in correspondence with the priorities dictated by the basic objectives outlined earlier. Heavy industries received the greatest emphasis; in the production of additional manufactured consumer goods, small enterprises get a roughly equal share with factory establishments; and the output in agriculture shows a significant increase of 20 per cent.

57. The national income calculations just outlined are based on the physical targets described earlier The physical targets themselves were based in most cases on the assumption of a 25 to 27 per cent increase in national income over five years or a 20 per cent increase in total consumption. (Allowance has to be made for greater investment.) The structure of the economy in 1960-61 as envisaged here, therefore, takes into account the increased expenditure on different goods and services as national output increase— after making allowance for such exchange of domestic goods for foreign goods as was implied in the physical targets set.

IV. The Pattern of Employment

58. The creation of adequate employment opportunities is one of the basic objectives of the Second Plan. Some of the implications of this policy have already been set forth earlier. In this section we may consider whether the target of 12 million additional persons to be pressed into gainful occupation outside agriculture can be realised in terms of the Plan envisaged here. Unfortunately, our knowledge of the occupational distribution of the population on the eve of the Second Plan can only be based on an extrapolation of the picture revealed by the 1951 census. This is not very satisfactory; but a rough estimate has been attempted to see where the additional persons might be absorbed.

59. In 1950-51, out of the total working force of 143.2 million persons, some 103.6 million were employed in agriculture and allied occupations. It is to the remaining 40 million persons—or say 42 to 43 million by 1955-56—employed in mines, factories, small enterprises, trade, transport, communications, professions and other salaried employees that some 12 million additional persons have to be added in the Second Plan. The likely results of the Plan outlined above may be analysed sector by sector.

(1) *Mining :* Some 8 lakh persons are employed in mines at present. With output from mines increasing by some 50 per cent in the Second Plan, additional employment in mines during the next plan period may be of the order of 3 to 4 lakhs.

17

(2) *Factory establishments :* Factory establishments employed some 30 lakh persons in 1950-51 of which roughly 24 lakhs were in consumer goods industries and the remaining in producer goods industries. (Total factory employment in 1955-56 may be a little higher than 30 lakhs.) In the Second Plan the net output of factory-produced consumer goods is expected to increase by some 20 per cent and of producer goods by 150 to 175 per cent. On this basis, additional employment in factories during the Second Plan may be of the order of 12 to 14 lakhs.

(3) *Small enterprises :* In 1950-51, small enterprises employed some 115 lakh persons. The term 'small enterprises' is, however, misleading. In addition to small-scale industries proper, it includes those engaged in construction of roads, buildings, irrigation works, carpenters, brick-layers etc. This latter category accounted for as much as 44 lakh persons out of the total of 115 lakhs in small enterprises. Among the rest, textiles and tailoring accounted for 32 lakhs, metal working and mechanical enterprises 12 lakhs and food and tobacco industries another 15 lakhs.

The Second Plan envisages an increase of about 40 per cent in the net output of small enterprises, ranging from 20 per cent in food industries and 25 per cent in leather products to 33 per cent in the metal group, 50 per cent in the textile and tailoring group and 60 per cent in the construction group. It is clear that income of persons employed in small enterprises is low and several of them do not have sufficient work. In this sector, therefore, employment cannot increase as fast as production. Assuming that employment increases, say by one-fourth as against a two-fifths increase in output, this sector would absorb about 30 lakh additional persons during the Second Plan.

(4) *Railways, communications, organized banks and insurance :* This sector provides employment to roughly 15 lakh persons in 1950-51. The Second Five Year Plan envisages considerable expansions in banking facilities, railways and communications. Additional employment of 3 to 5 lakh persons here may, therefore, reasonably be expected.

(5) *Other commerce and transport*: This sector is a great employment provider. Some 95 lakh persons were engaged in this sector in 1950-51. Nearly two-thirds of this group are employed in retail trade, some 6 lakhs in wholesale trade, 10 to 11 lakhs in hotels and restaurants and about the same number in road transport.

If net output of this sector increases by 20 to 25 per cent, as is envisaged, additional gainful occupation for some 20 lakh additional persons should reasonably be available in this sector. It is arguable that we should not rely on trade for additional employment in as much as this sector is already rather large in relation to the total size of the economy. However, for the immediate future some expansion of employment in trade is to be expected.

(6) *Government administration:* In 1950-51, there were 39 lakh persons employed in Government administration, and additional employment in this sector during the Second Plan may be of the order of some 5 lakhs.

(7) *Professions and liberal arts :* This is another important sector from the point of view of employment. In 1950-51 some 64 lakh persons were employed in this sector including some 10 lakh teachers, 11 to 12 lakh barbers, 12 to 13 lakh dhobis, 7 lakh scavengers and 8 lakh medical practitioners and health workers.[1]

60. In view of the substantial increase in the expenditure on health, sanitation and education envisaged in the Second Plan and the increased demand for the services of barbers, dhobis etc., an increase in employment by 15 lakhs or more in this sector is not unlikely.

61. To sum up, the additional employment we may count on for the Second Plan is as follows[2].

INCREASE IN EMPLOYMENT

sector	increase in employment 1955-56 to 1960-61 (in lakhs)
(2)	(2)
mines	3 to 4
factories	12 to 14
small enterprises (including construction workers)	30
railways, communications, etc.	3 to 4
other commerce & transport	20
government administration	5
professions and liberal arts	15 to 20
total	88 to 97

[1] The juxtaposition of barbers and dhobis with teachers and doctors is rather curious, but it is retained here in as much as it corresponds to national income classification in India.

[2] In view of the particularly urgent problem of urban unemployment among the educated middle-classes, we must also indicate how much employment is likely to be created for this sector. But it has not been possible to attempt this considering the several arbitrary assumptions involved.

62.   Thus, the foreseeable employment potential of the Plan is of the order of 9 to 9.5 million persons absorbed outside agriculture. The Second Five Year Plan, therefore, has to be at least as bold as the one envisaged in this paper if it is to fulfil the promise of fuller employment. Perhaps some one to two million persons would be added to those engaged in agriculture in any case in view of their existing occupations. Again, not all the persons employed in agriculture and allied pursuits depend on land. Some additional employment among those engaged in fishing, forestry or sheep-raising may not be undesirable.

63.   It should be emphasized, however, that the increase in employment envisaged here will demand a great deal of organization, besides finance and suitable policies. It is clear that small enterprises, for example, which bear the brunt of the employment effort will not expand on the scale envisaged without sustained effort. Creation of employment opportunities is not a matter of providing 'jobs' and the outcome will depend greatly on the response of the public. Provision of employment also carries with it the implication that training facilities for the type of personnel needed would be provided for on the scale required. Again in several sectors we have assumed that additional output would mean a more or less proportionate increase in employment. This envisages some control over excessive rationalization, on concentration of units, and on frittering away of higher demand in raising the remuneration of those already in employment to the detriment of the unemployed. The problem of unemployment, as has already been emphasized, can hardly be separated from that of distribution of income.

64.   From this point of view, it may be of interest to note the following figures about the net output per person employed in different sectors. The figures must be interpreted with caution. Thus, figures in money terms do not take into account differences in cost of living or of the non-economic disabilities and advantages of certain occupations or places. Again, net output per employed persons represents the earnings of labour as well as capital and does not take Government draft into consideration. The differences among sectors are partly the result of different capital requirements per unit of output. What is more, the number of persons gainfully occupied per household varies from sector to sector, and the disparities in income per occupied person do not correspond to disparities in incomes per

household[1]. The occupational distribution envisaged for 1955-56 and 1960-61 is also largely conjectural. Nonetheless, the table below illustrates an important aspect of the Second Plan. It may be noted that the distribution of additional output and employment in the Second Plan is so designed, by and large, as to raise levels of living at lower levels.

OCCUPATIONAL PATTERN IN INDIA

sector	working force (in millions)			net output per occupied person (Rs. per year at 1952-53 prices)		
	1950-51	1955-56	1960-61 estimated	1950-51	1955-56	1960-61 estimated
(1)	(2)	(3)	(4)	(5)	(6)	(7)
1. agriculture and allied pursuits	103.6	109.6	111.0	436	482	571
2. mining and factory establishments	3.8	4.0	5.7	1,737	2,250	2,632
3. small enterprises	11.5	12.0	15.0	809	850	953
4. communications, railways, banks and insurance	1.5	1.6	2.0	2,067	2,250	2,350
5. other commerce and transport	9.5	10.0	12.0	1,410	1,510	1,567
6. govt. administration, professions, liberal arts and the rest	13.3	14.9	17.3	1,075	1,161	1,202
total	143.2	152.0	163.0	642	710	840

65. Net output per occupied person increases by only 4 or 5 per cent in the tertiary sector where it is already high compared with the national average. In the case of agriculture and small scale industries, the increase is of the order of 20 and 12 per cent respectively. Mining and factory establishments also show an increase in net output per employed person of some one-sixth. This increase reflects, however, the shift in favour of heavy industries where large amounts of capital are associated with a comparatively small employment of labour. Thus, by and large, the employment pattern envisaged here is in keeping with the basic objectives of fuller employment and social justice.

---

[1] Thus the ratio of earners to non-earners in a household in 1951 was 1 : 1.4 for agriculture; 1 : 1.3 for production in rural areas other than cultivation; 1 : 2.1 for commerce; 1 : 1.8 for transport; 1 : 1.7 for other services; and 1 : 1.7 for production other than cultivation in urban areas.

Chapter Three

FINANCIAL RESOURCES FOR THE PLAN

*   *   *   *   *

Savings and Investments

2. If net investment of the order of Rs. 5,600 crores is to be realized over the next plan period, savings of the same order must be forthcoming. With increased incomes, the volume of savings is bound to increase. For initiating a process of higher investment and higher incomes by fuller utilization of unemployed and under-utilized resources, it is not necessary that savings come first and only these are invested later. Credit has to be taken in advance for the additional savings that are likely to arise as incomes and investment increase. Some initial credit creation, therefore, is an essential part of a development programme. Nonetheless, if planned investments are to be realised without generating serious inflationary pressures, the initial credit creation must be limited with reference to what savings are likely to be available or can be created by suitable policy measures.

3. An investment programme of Rs. 5,600 crores for the Second Plan cannot be carried through without a considerable increase in the rate of savings in the community. Assuming that sterling balances can be drawn down by some Rs. 100 or 150 crores and foreign assistance of the order of Rs. 500 crores is available during the Second Plan, domestic savings of the order of Rs. 5,000 crores must be available. The Taxation Enquiry Commission has estimated that total savings in India in 1953-54 and total net investment (at home and abroad) amounted to some seven per cent of national income. Their concept of net investment is not strictly comparable to the one used here in arriving at the net investmet of Rs. 5,600 crores for the Second Plan. Thus, unlike the TEC, we have excluded non-monetized investment. At the same time, we have made some allowance for investment in stocks and in small enterprises which have been disregarded by the TEC. Again a sizeable increase in public investment is expected for the last two

years of the First Plan. On the other hand, the TEC's estimate of net investment abroad of Rs. 70 crores in 1953:54 must be regarded as rather exceptional. Normally, we should expect a deficit in our current balance of payments (not taking credit for donations) with the result that the total investment in the country must be higher than domestic savings. Taking these considerations into account, it is reasonable to expect that comparable to the figure of Rs. 5,600 cores for the Second Plan, net investment in the country in 1955-56 would be of the order of 6.75 per cent of national income and corresponding domestic savings of some 6 per cent of national income. On this basis, the growth in investment and savings over the Second Plan would have to be somewhat as follows :

GROWTH IN INVESTMENT AND SAVINGS

(Rs. crores)

		1955-56	1956-57	1957-58	1958-59	1959-60	1960-61	2nd plan 1956-57 to 1960-61
	(1)	(2)	(3)	(4)	(5)	(6)	(7)	(8)
(a)	national income	10,800	11,300	11,825	12,375	13,000	13,700	62,200
(b)	net investment	730	810	930	1,060	1,300	1,500	5,600
(c)	domestic savings	650	680	800	930	1,170	1,370	4,950
(d)	foreign resources	80	130	130	130	130	130	650

4. The phasing over the five years of savings and investment given above is intended to be illustrative. The essential point is that in order to achieve a total investment of Rs. 5,600 crores, the rate of investment must increase from 6.75 per cent of national income in 1955-56 to 11 per cent of national income in 1960-61, and domestic savings from 6 to 10 per cent over the same period. If foreign resources are not available on the scale envisaged, the savings effort at home would have to be correspondingly greater.

5. Whether an increase in the rate of domestic savings from 6 per cent in the beginning of the next plan period to 10 per cent by 1960-61 is likely to take place in response to a voluntary increase in savings resulting from additional incomes cannot be judged in advance. The increase in savings envisaged here is not very large

in relation to the rates achieved in other countries. But, considering the current low rate of savings and the large margin of unsatisfied needs, it may be assumed that savings of the order required would not be forthcoming without special and persistent effort at restricting consumption through fiscal and other devices.

6.   In an underdeveloped economy, where there are idle resources, increased investment need not imply a reduction in current consumption.   It would, however, imply austerity, that is, preparedness to hold down consumption, especially of luxuries, in the face of rising incomes.   A check on the consumption of non-essential commodities, domestic as well as imported, is necessary in order to release additional resources for the production of essential goods.   Shortages of essential goods are dealt with better in this way than by direct limitation of consumption.   However, if resources released through restriction of luxury consumption are not of much use for increasing the supplies of essential goods, controls over consumption of essentials would become unavoidable.   The question of controls must, in other words, be judged in terms of the particular real resources, which are in short supply.   Foreign exchange resources have to be conserved with particular care, in that they can be converted into whatever commodities become scarce within the country.   In the present world situation in regard to food and cotton, one can hope that a plan of the magnitude contemplated can be seen through without having to impose controls on necessaries like food and cloth.

7.   Up to a point, the emergence of some inflationary pressures or a sellers' market is necessary, since our objective is to push ahead as far as possible in the direction of utilizing our resources.   Essentially inflationary pressures—or insufficiency of savings— arise as a result of inelastic supplies of goods against which people direct their demand.   The elasticity of supply is not equally great in the case of all commodities.   With effort and organization, it can be altered favourably at least in selected sectors.   If we are to stop at the first bottleneck in supplies for fear of a rise in prices in that sector, even though supplies in other sectors are elastic to some extent, we are likely to stop short of the full potential for expansion of the economy.   We have to be prepared to 'tackle' short supplies in some commodities.   Whether in doing so we would be able to prevent a general and cumulative rise in prices depends, obviously, upon the measure of shortage and the organizational efficiency in dealing with it.   In an expanding economy the

sufficiency of savings cannot be predicted in advance, but since the overall effort suggested is not excessive and is required for making an impact on employment, the practical problem is one of watching overall economic trends and of correcting through fiscal and other measures any shortage in resources in particular sectors as they arise.

8. From the stand-point of finding resources for the public sector, it is necessary to consider not only the outlay on the Plan but total outlay. Expenditure outside the Plan has an obvious significance to the realistic appraisal of the financing of the Plan. The outlay on the Plan in the public sector includes, first of all, all expenditure which results in the creation of new capital assets (directly in the public or indirectly in the private sector). In addition, it should include that part of the current expenditure on specific developmental heads which represents an increase over the level reached at the end of the First Plan. This would give a clear idea of the 'lift' we are giving to the developmental effort during the next plan. This is the concept which has been kept in mind in this paper in arriving at the plan outlay of Rs. 4,300 crores.

9. An alternative would be to include all expenditure under specified developmental heads in the Plan, leaving out only expenditure on non-developmental items like Defence and Civil Administration. Although this would inflate the Plan figures, it would facilitate a more realistic appraisal of the Plan and its financing by ruling out the possibility of shifting of expenditure, as from one-sub-category to the other within the broad category of developmental heads. It would also enable a quicker review of the progress under the Plan from the budget itself. On the other hand, by confining the scope of the Plan to the schemes deemed more essential to further effort, we are better able to scrutinize them. The best course under the circumstances would, therefore, be to high-light *both* the total expenditure under specified developmental heads and the outlay on the Plan. As a rough approximation, the budgetary position of the Centre and the States combined may be outlined as in the table on page 138.

10. The estimated outlay of the Centre and the State Governments combined for 1955-56 is based on the budget proposals for the year, as far as possible, and on the revised budget figures for 1954-55. However, in view of the difficulties in combining the figures for the Centre and the States and in apportioning the development outlay, within the Plan and outside the Plan, the estimates must be taken only as roughly indicative of the magnitudes involved.

TOTAL GOVERNMENT EXPENDITURE

(Rs. Crores—estimates)

	1955-56	1960-61	over second plan 1956-57 to 1960-61
(1)	(2)	(3)	(4)
1. outside the plan			
(a) non-developmental	625	725	3400
(b) developmental	220	225	1100
sub-total	825	950	4500
2. on the plan	600	1100	4300
total	1524	2050	8800

11.   It is assumed that public outlay on the Plan will increase from Rs. 600 crores or so in 1955-56 to Rs. 1,100 crores in 1960-61, *i.e.* by about 80%, in order to make up a total of Rs. 4,300 crores over the plan period.   Expenditure outside the Plan is assumed to increase by 15% over the five years or by Rs. 25 crores every year.   The total outlay on developmental heads is envisaged to be of the order of Rs. 5,400 crores—Rs. 4,300 crores in the Plan, and Rs. 1,100 crores outside the Plan.

12.   The question is how a total Government outlay of Rs. 8,800 crores (Rs. 4,500 crores outside the Plan and Rs. 4,300 crores·on the Plan) is to be financed.   Assuming that the Government takes some 8.5 per cent of national income in taxes and in non-tax revenue as has been the case on an average over the past four or five years (7% in taxes and about 1.5 per cent in non-tax revenue) the total revenue receipts would amount to above Rs.5,200 crores. Borrowing from the public may possibly yield (net) another Rs.1,000 crores (about Rs. 600 crores from loans and Rs. 400 crores from small savings).   Contribution from railways may be put at Rs. 200 crores over five years, The budgetary position of the Government over the Second Plan might, therefore, look somewhat as follows :

expenditure	(Rs. crores)	receipts	(Rs. crores)	deficit (Rs. crores)
		on revenue account	5,200	
on the plan	4,300	from railways	200	
outside the plan	4,500	loans from the people	1,000	
	8,800		6,400	2,400

13.   As against the gap or deficit of Rs. 2,400 crores, we may take credit for some Rs. 400 crores of foreign assistance.*   Over the First Plan, foreign assistance utilized in the public sector is likely to be of the order of Rs. 250 crores.   Thus we are assuming a 60 per cent increase in the amount of external assistance utilized by the public sector.

14.   The remaining gap of Rs. 2,000 crores cannot be filled up by deficit financing or creation of money.   As a first approximation, we may assume that such money creation can be resorted to the extent of Rs. 1,000 to Rs. 1,200 crores by the Government.   Allow- ance must also be made for credit creation by banks for the needs of the private sector, say Rs. 400 crores or so, bringing total credit creation to Rs. 1,400 to Rs. 1,600 crores.   A part of this credit would be withdrawn from the system as we use up our accumulated sterling balances.   We made an allowance earlier for a decline in our foreign exchange reserves by some Rs. 150 crores.   Even then, total money supply in the economy might increase by some Rs. 1,300 crores during the Second Plan.   We have argued earlier that credit creation is essential to development and that some price rises may well occur in an economy trying to reach to the full limit of its resources.   In India, a larger money supply will be needed as the monetized sector expands relatively to the non-monetized sector. Even then, with a 25 to 27 per cent increase in national income, an increase in money supply by some Rs. 1,300 crores on a base of some Rs. 2,000 crores must be regarded as short of the outside limit.

15.   If, then, for the reasons just stated deficit financing by the Government must be restricted to some Rs. 1,000 to Rs. 1,200 crores, it would be necessary to raise at least Rs. 800 crores by increased taxation, or by compulsory borrowings, or through increased profit of Government enterprises.   In fact, a combination of all these will be called for.   If additional Government profits are to be raised, it might be necessary for the State to enter into the field of trading or production of consumer goods.   The scope for such expansion of State activity into profit-making ventures will have to be carefully examined.   Alternatively, taxation in the country will have to be raised from some 7 per cent of national income to 9 or 10 per cent of national income by 1960-61.   An increase in taxation from 7 to

---

* In addition, foreign assistance of Rs. 100 crores is envisaged for the private sector.

9 or even 10 per cent of national income cannot be regarded as excessive if our aim is to have a bolder plan which requires an increase in the savings of the community from 6 to 10 per cent of national income. But it should be borne in mind that some tax adjustments will be necessary even to maintain the existing level of tax receipts at 7 per cent of national income.

16. The foregoing discussion of the resources for the public sector has been in terms of the receipts and expenditures of the Centre and the States combined. A survey of the financial position of individual States during the Second Plan will have to be prepared separately.

RESOURCES FOR THE PRIVATE SECTOR

17. Of the total investment of Rs. 2,200 crores in the private sector, Rs. 1,100 crores is envisaged in construction; Rs. 500 crores in industry, mining and transport; Rs. 200 crores in agriculture; and Rs. 400 crores in working capital in trade and industry and in residual items.

18. The Taxation Enquiry Commission has estimated that net investment in organized enterprises (public limited and private limited companies) and in private transport amounted to Rs. 75 crores in 1953-54. Correspondingly, corporate savings and new subscription to capital of companies together have also been put at Rs. 75 crores for that year. This investment is roughly comparable to the provision made here for an investment of Rs. 500 crores in industries, mining and transport in the private sector for the next plan period. An increase in the rate of such investment from Rs. 75 crores in 1953-54 to an average of Rs. 100 crores over the next plan may be regarded as feasible, particularly in view of the larger profits that are likely to arise in organized industries if un-utilized capacity is put to full use. The more important problem would be to ensure a proper allocation of the investment in the private organized sector of industries. Apart from capital issues control and export and import controls, a differential tax policy might be needed in this context. Where necessary, arrangements may be made for loans or planned increases in prices for realising important investments in this sector.

19. The requirements of working capital for industry and trade can be met without much difficulty through bank accommodation. We have made allowance for an increase of some Rs. 400 crores in bank credit earlier in arriving at total credit creation in the eco-

nomy. Indeed, with deficit financing of Rs. 1,000 to Rs. 1,200 crores in the public sector, the problem may well be one of preventing excessive bank accommodation.

20. Of the net investment in the private sector of Rs. 2,200 crores, about one-half is envisaged to be in construction. This implies private construction activity of the order of Rs. 220 crores per year on an average in the next plan period. Private monetized construction at present may be estimated at about Rs. 150 to 160 crores per year. The source of savings for construction activity cannot be indicated. Nor can it be asserted that the increase in construction activity envisaged would, in fact, be realized. If aggregate savings are inadequate, there is no knowing where this shortage would impinge. As long as investment in the higher priority part of the private sector is assured, any shortfall in the availability of resources for other purposes would not seriously retard the tempo of development.

BALANCE OF PAYMENTS

21. A close analysis of the balance of payments position for the Second Plan period has yet to be made. Considering the type and structure of our exports, it is doubtful if a large increase in earnings can be secured, at least in the earlier years of the Plan. In the targets indicated earlier, provision has been made for larger exports of cotton textile, tea, mica, manganese and some of the newer products like sewing machines, electrical goods, etc. However, in view of the increasing competition in some export items, it might be safe not to assume any significant increase in export earnings. The balance would turn mainly on imports.

22. Of the total investment of Rs. 5,600 crores, about Rs. 2,500 crores will be of a kind that makes little demand on foreign exchange. For the rest, that is, about Rs. 3,000 crores of investment in irrigation and power, communications, industries, railways, etc., if we assume the imported component at 33 to 40 per cent (as a very rough average), the import requirements would work out at between Rs. 1,000 and Rs. 1,200 crores. To this we may add Rs. 400 crores or so as imports needed for replacement.

23. Total imports of capital goods over the Second Plan period may thus amount to Rs. 1,400 to 1,600 crores. At present, these imports are of the order of Rs. 100 crores a year. Since the overall external account is more or less in balance, it may be assumed that we could finance Rs. 500 crores worth of machinery and equipment

imports from current earnings. The problem, then, would be to find foreign exchange resources of the order of Rs. 1,000 crores. Allowing for a saving of foreign exchange of some Rs. 200 crores on petrol, raw cotton, sugar and similar items where domestic production is expected to increase, there would still be a problem of finding Rs. 800 crores of foreign exchange. The foreign exchange assets held by the Reserve Bank can perhaps be drawn down by Rs. 100 to 150 crores during the next plan period (*i.e.*, from the present level of Rs. 730 crores to 550 or 600 crores, after making an allowance for a decline of Rs. 30 crores or so in the last year of the First Plan). This leaves a balance of Rs. 650-700 crores. If Rs. 500 crores of this could be met by way of external assistance, there will still be need for economising on imports and for promotion of exports. Since the reducible element in our imports is small, there is a correspondingly greater need for increasing exports.

THE SECOND FIVE YEAR PLAN

A MEMORANDUM PREPARED BY THE PANEL OF ECONOMISTS,* PLANNING COMMISSION

Covering letter dated New Delhi, 10 April, 1955 from Professor D. R. Gadgil, Vice-chairman of the Panel of Economists, submitting the Memorandum to Shri C. D. Deshmukh, Chairman of the Panel.

In submitting the accompanying Memorandum, we would like to point out that the time at our disposal did not permit us to make an exhaustive study of the numerous papers placed before us both by our colleagues and by others nor to have a full and thorough discussion of the numerous issues involved. We regard this Memorandum as an interim document, pending fuller study on several points we have only briefly touched upon. We hope that we shall have occasion later to go into greater detail on some of the items included in this Memorandum. In the meanwhile, we have given our best possible consideration to the various questions connected with the Plan-Frame that we could within the time at our disposal, and the Memorandum that accompanies this letter represents the broad consensus of opinion reached at our meetings. One of our colleagues, Prof. B. R. Shenoy, has differences of opinion on some points and proposed to submit a separate note as soon as possible.

The Panel of Economists consists of :
(1) C. D. Deshmukh, *Minister of Finance and Member, Planning Commission— (Chairman)* ; (2) D. R. Gadgil, *Director, Gokhale School of Economics & Politics, Poona—(Vice-chairman)* ; (3) A. K. Das Gupta, *Professor of Economics, Banaras University* ; (4) M. L. Dantwala, *Member-Secretary, Research Programmes Committee, Planning Commission* ; (5) B. N. Datar, *Director, Labour & Employment Division, Planning Commission* ; (6) B. N. Ganguli, *Delhi School of Economics* ; (7) L. C. Jain, *Professor of Economics, Saugor University* ; (8) J. V. Joshi, *Executive Director, Reserve Bank of India, Bombay* ; (9) D. G. Karve, *Director, Programmes Evaluation Organization, Planning Commission* ; (10) Bala Krishna, *Professor of Economics, University of Madras* ; (11) D. T. Lakdawala, *Professor of Economics, University of Bombay* ; (12) B. K. Madan, *Economic Adviser, Reserve Bank of India, Bombay* ; (13) S. K. Muranjan, *Principal, Sydenham College of Commerce, Bombay* ; (14) J. P. Niyogi, *Professor of Economics, University of Calcutta* ; (15) V. R. Pillai, *Professor of Economics, University of Travancore, Trivandrum* ; (16) K. N. Raj, *Professor of Monetary Economics, Delhi School of Economics* ; (17) V. K. R. V. Rao, *Director, Delhi School of Economics* ; (18) D. S. Savkar, *Director of Banking Research, Reserve Bank of India, Bombay* ; (19) S. R. Sen, *Economic & Statistical Adviser, Ministry of Food & Agriculture, New Delhi* ; (20) B. R. Shenoy, *Professor of Economics, University of Gujrat, Ahmedabad* ; (21) C. N. Vakil, *Director, School of Economics & Sociology, University of Bombay* ; (22) J. J. Anjaria, *Chief, Economic Division, Planning Commission—(Secretary).*

BASIC CONSIDERATIONS RELATING
TO THE PLAN-FRAME

The Panel of Economists had its third session on the 8th, 9th and 10th April to consider the main issues relating to the preparation of a plan-frame. The issues grouped themselves under three broad heads :—

(i)   size of the Second Five Year Plan;

(ii) structure and content of the Plan;

(iii) policy and institutional implications of the plan-frame proposed.

These questions were considered by the Panel in the light of a large number of papers — about forty—received from its members and, also in the light of the papers prepared by the economists and statisticians in Government and the Reserve Bank and at the Indian Statistical Institute. This memorandum sets out the main conclusions reached by the Panel on these issues.

I. SIZE OF THE PLAN

2. The Panel subscribes to the view that a bolder plan for the second five-year period is both necessary for dealing with the large problems of poverty and unemployment and under-employment and feasible in view of the momentum gained during the First Five Year Plan. The Second Five Year Plan must not only provide for a more rapid increase in aggregate national income; it must make an advance towards the declared goal of a socialistic pattern of society. It is important, in other words, to secure simultaneous and balanced progress in the direction of raising living standards, increasing employment opportunities and reducing economic and social inequalities. The problem, therefore, is not merely one of stepping up the rate of investment in the economy—though that is necessary and important; but of securing an optimum increase of production and employment together with a wider measure of social justice. A bolder plan is, obviously, not merely a bigger plan; it must be one which is motivated by a bolder economic and social philosophy. Necessarily, it calls for a much greater effort

and contribution by all classes of the community and presents a much greater challenge of organization and administrative achievement. The Panel also wishes to emphasize the fact that clear decisions on the policy and institutional implications of a bolder plan are essential at the very outset if the several objectives and targets are to be realized.

3. The question of the size of the Plan may be considered with reference to the order of increase in national income (or production) on the average which should be aimed at during the Second Plan period, the employment objectives which should be borne in view and the resources which could be available for the financing of the Plan.

4. We consider that the Second Five Year Plan should aim at securing an increase in national income of about 25 per cent in the course of five years. If allowance is made for favourable monsoons the increase in national income during the period of the First Plan is likely, on the basis of figures upto 1953-54, to be of the order of 12 to 13 per cent. The rate of increase proposed to be aimed at in the Second Plan period is thus roughly double of that attained during the First Plan. We have observed the rates of increase in the national income of other countries over different periods and consider that, given a determined bid to put forth a maximum measure of effort, this rate of increase can be attained. It is clear that if such a big advance in the rate of increase of national income is to be achieved, a considerable stepping up of the tempo of development is indispensable. That the higher average rate proposed for the Second Plan is, however, not unattainable is indicated by the mounting scale of the development effort from year to year, as judged by the rate of investment, during the First Plan period.

5. The rate of increase in national income aimed at is partly set by the employment objectives. The Planning Commission has indicated to the Panel that the Plan must provide for a creation of new opportunities for gainful employment for at least the additions that will take place to the labour force in the five-year period as a result of the increase in population. The minimum new employment target must, therefore, be the absorption of 9 to 10 million workers. Considering that, in addition, some at least of the existing under-employed have to be given fuller employment, the employment target of the Plan has, in fact, to be higher.

6. We may, in this connection, stress a few salient points regarding the present occupational structure. Agriculture and cottage

19

industries together account for about 75 per cent of the working force and carry a large amount of excess manpower. There is, therefore, little hope of any substantial absorption of the new increase in the labour force in these lines. New opportunities of the order of 10 or 12 million jobs have thus to be created on a base of some 30-40 million of the existing labour force employed in the secondary and tertiary sectors. The Plan has to provide for substantial investment in heavy industry, but such investment is by nature capital-intensive; it cannot absorb large numbers of workers. It is not possible in the short period to bring into being a new employment structure which would afford stable job opportunities on an adequate scale. It is necessary at this stage, therefore, to increase the opportunities for revolving employment in construction and public works activity and so to plan this activity that it leaves behind, through additions to the society's productive equipment, a significant amount of permanent employment. Simultaneously, through programmes aimed at maintaining and increasing the demand for simpler types of labour-intensive industries, the scope for durable employment in the field of industrial production may also be expanded.

7. For raising national income by some 25 per cent over the five-year period, investment in the economy will have to be stepped up from the present level of about 7 per cent of national income to about 11 per cent by the end of the next plan period. This is not too high a target, but it is fairly ambitious. It implies, on an average a 50 per cent stepping up of the rate of investment and hence of savings (except to the relatively small extent to which resources from abroad can be obtained to supplement domestic savings). In terms of the total volume of investment the next Plan would have to provide for about double the investment in the First Plan. We should like to stress that the effort involved in this increase is considerable, and will strain the economy a very great deal.

8. We have reviewed broadly in this context the papers placed before us by the official economists on estimates of financial resources for the Second Plan. The papers bring out clearly the fact that considerable fresh taxation will be necessary even for ensuring that tax revenue maintains its present share of about 7 per cent of national income. Given the order of the proposed Plan, however, we think that something like 9 per cent of national income will have to be directed into the national fisc in the form of total taxation, if deficit financing is to be kept within safe limits. We consider that the

estimates of the likely receipts from public borrowings and small savings are capable of being realized, with the necessary drive.

9.   We wish to stress in this connection the need for full and speedy implementation of the recommendations of the Taxation Enquiry Commission for mobilizing the resources needed for development. Our present tax structure is not such as to ensure even a proportionate increase in tax receipts as national income goes up. What is needed, however, is more than this—an increase in the proportion of national income that becomes available to the public sector. The measures recommended by the Taxation Enquiry Commission for a widening and deepening of the tax structure have, therefore, to be implemented expeditiously, and tax administration has to be strengthened to enable it to cope with the additional work and effectively to minimize evasion. We note, however, that the Taxation Enquiry Commission in framing its recommendations, proceeded on the assumption of a total size of the next Plan for the public sector (viz. Rs. 3,500 crores) which was significantly smaller than is now proposed (viz. Rs. 4,300 crores) on a fuller consideration of the objectives of increasing production and employment. Even if the scope for deficit financing is now assessed somewhat less rigorously, the higher order of the proposed Plan compared to what the Taxation Enquiry Commission assumed indicates the large measure of fiscal effort that would be required *beyond* the recommendations of the Taxation Enquiry Commission, if significant inflationary effects are to be avoided. An urgent summary review of the measures necessary to step up the tax effort is, therefore, necessary. When the plan-frame is adopted and a clearer picture is available of the extent and composition of the increases in national income that are likely to take place, the tax measures that would be appropriate to the increase in poduction could be worked out more precisely. An analysis of the investment structure of the tentative plan-frame to which we refer in more detail in the next section of this memorandum, indicates that much of the largest part of increase in industrial production would occur in producers' goods and small-scale cottage industries, neither of which would significantly expand the base of existing direct or indirect taxes in the period of the Second Plan. Owing to the employment bias of the other components of the Plan, too, the largest short term increase in incomes would be in the form of wages of workers on construction and public works, including irrigation projects, or of agricultural producers. This emphasizes the great difficulty of increasing tax

proceeds unless a fundamental revision in some current concepts that underlie the tax system is accepted. One of these concepts relates to the exemption of essentials from the scope of an important part of commodity taxation. When so large a measure of effort is necessary to increase the *proportion* of tax revenues to national income, which has remained so obstinately static, one cannot escape the logic of the fact that the mass of consumption is by the mass of the people. Unless this bears a somewhat higher burden of taxation, no perceptible change in the stubborn ratio of public revenues to national income can be achieved. We wish to endorse, in particular, the recommendation of the Taxation Enquiry Commission to the effect that Article 286(3) of the Constitution may be amended to remove the present exemption of articles "essential to the life of the community" from the scope of State sales taxation. Simultaneously, measures to secure a practical ceiling on incomes through a steepening of taxes on income and wealth, including estate duties, become an imperative necessity. A revision of the price policy of important public enterprises with a view to obtaining a larger surplus as a contribution to the resources for economic development is similarly required. Besides, the general increase in rates of direct and indirect taxation that will be involved in the considerable stepping up of tax effort will be part of the challenge to administrative efficiency that the big development effort for putting through the next Plan entails.

10. The extent to which recourse may be had to deficit financing will determine the magnitude of the efforts through alternative means of mobilizing resources for the financing of the Plan. In an economy in which planned development is being undertaken a part of the expenditure in planned development is being currently or within a short time reflected in increase in current production. There is, therefore, an increment in total production against which it is possible to increase money supply within the community. No close and invariable relation as to the desirable measure of increase in money supply with increase in production can, however, be postulated, especially in an economy which is neither fully integrated nor fully monetized as the Indian. Even so it is reasonable to state that with a constantly increasing level of national income an addition to money supply may not only not have inflationary consequences, but may be required to prevent a decline in prices which may lead to distress and distortions in the economy.

11. Deficit financing is thus not necessarily always dangerous; it is the timing and magnitude of it that is of crucial importance. Deficit financing undertaken while the economy is already under inflationary pressure, or in such volume as will rapidly generate inflationary effects, has to be avoided. It appears to us that at present there is no general inflationary pressure in the economy. We do not, therefore, see any danger in undertaking deficit financing in a limited measure at the beginning of the Second Five Year Plan period. For a year or two, deficit financing at a rate of Rs. 200 crores or so is safe—and even necessary. But, continuous deficit financing on this scale for a number of years is certain to generate inflationary pressures. A bolder plan with an emphasis on employment and heavy industry has inevitably a large inflation potential. We should like at this stage to caution against any tendency to undue optimism as regards the extent to which the use of deficit financing may avoid the awkward necessity of a deliberate endeavour to mobilize resources, as a result of the apparently large budgetary deficits of recent years not having produced adverse consequences. Firstly, the deficits have not been as large as originally envisaged in budget proposals. Secondly, there has been an unexpected—if not entirely adventitious—increase in food-grains production. It is impossible to forecast the total national and international economic situation at this stage. We cannot, therefore, say with certainty that the situation will remain equally favourable throughout the Plan period. The undertaking of deficit financing may itself change the situation unless counteracted by a rapid pace of development or by international conditions. We feel it necessary to suggest, therefore, that the strictest watch be kept on the situation. Any indication that inflationary pressures are developing must be met by timely and suitable action to keep it under check. We do not suggest that the Plan should be changed immediately because some inflationary signs are observed. The immediate step would be to take appropriate action to keep inflation in check and have elaborate plans ready for the event of a further increase in inflationary pressure. These plans may involve imposition of financial and physical controls, and if there is no readiness to face this possibility, deficit financing would not be safe. It would be equally necessary at the same time to re-examine the financial plan to see whether it is not possible to increase the resources available to Government in other directions. On the whole, we do not recommend deficit financing of a larger extent than that indicated by the figure of Rs. 1000 crores

for five years and are of opinion that the situation in this regard should be kept under watch and should in any case be re-examined at the end of the second year or at the midpoint of the Plan period.

12. The pattern of investments in the Second Plan indicates that a very considerable increase in imports of capital equipment and machinery will be necessary. This will undoubtedly entail a heavy strain on the balance of payments. Such estimates as are available of the foreign exchange financing of the Plan indicate that foreign assistance to the tune of over Rs. 600 crores will be required for the Plan period, if a draft on foreign reserves is to be avoided. In our opinion, foreign reserves should be kept for unforeseen emergencies or as a safeguard against miscarriage of calculations and not committed to any significant extent in respect of planned expenditure.

II. STRUCTURE AND CONTENT

13. We have considered the size of the Plan in the previous section and indicated the measure of the effort for mobilizing the resources required for the purpose. It is now necessary to examine the Plan from the point of view of its structure, the pattern of investment it contemplates, the effect it will have on employment, and the kind of relationship that it postulates between different sectors of the economy for the purpose of securing internal consistency.

14. Broadly speaking, it is the intention of the Plan to maximize employment and capital formation, and increase consumption, consistently with the magnitude of the suggested overall increase in national income by 25 per cent over the five year period. Obviously, we want to make the greatest possible impression on unemployment and under-employment in the country, but the employment provided must be such as not only to lead to an increase in national income by 25 per cent, but also to see that the increase is distributed in such directions as to lead to the desired quantum of increase in both capital goods and in consumption goods. Without the former, there can be no real increase in productivity or in the capacity for further and accelerated growth in the economy; without the latter, there will be no immediate change in the level of living, no incentive or enthusiasm for popular effort, and every danger of the emergence of inflation and a consequent breakdown of the programme for development. We must, therefore, make an appropriate division between saving and consumption from the additional incomes generated by the Plan. Having done this we have to see

that the investment outlay not only leads to the desired increase in consumption goods and services, but also to such increases in capital goods and services as will not only be consistent with the needs of consumption goods industries but also lead to an increase in productivity, facilitate the growth of capital equipment from domestic resources, and make for an accelerated growth in the output of consumption goods in subsequent Plan periods.

15. Let us first take up the question of investment. The tentative Plan-frame contemplates an investment outlay of Rs. 5,600 crores during the five year period together with current expenditure by Government of Rs. 900 crores on development services, the latter figure being exclusive of the level of development expenditure expected to be reached at the end of the First Plan period. The broad pattern of the proposed investment outlay of Rs. 5,600 crores is visualized as under :—

ALLOCATION OF NET INVESTMENT IN THE ECONOMY

sector	rupees crores	percentage of total
(1)	(2)	(3)
1. agriculture and community development (including irrigation and flood (control)	950	17.1
2. power	500	8.9
3. transport and communications	900	16.1
4. industries and mining (including small-scale) ..	1400	25.0
5. construction (house, ships, schools, hospitals, etc.) ..	1350	24.0
6. stocks and miscellaneous	500	8.9
total ..	5600	100.0

16. We are generally in agreement with the investment pattern outlined in the preceding table. We are obviously not in a position to comment on the technical accuracy of the actual figures given under each head of investment; in fact, this cannot be determined except through a process of detailed examination at the technical level of the individual projects included in the investment outlay and we presume this will be done by the Planning Commission during the coming months. But the greater weight that the investment pattern assigns to industry and mining has our full approval.

17. In saying this, however, we do not want to underestimate the importance of agriculture in our economy. Agriculture will for long remain the most important economic activity of our people; and without an adequate supply of food and raw materials, there can be no economic development. But there is no denying the fact that the First Plan has laid a solid base for the development of agriculture, and while a part of the large increase that has taken place in agricultural production is due to favourable weather, a part is certainly due to the creation of better facilities for increasing production. The Second Plan continues the process and is designed further to strengthen the agricultural base of the economy. But the very development of agriculture beyond a certain stage requires the development of non-agricultural activities, specially of industry, not only for providing markets for the increased agricultural produce but also for providing the supplies of industrial consumer goods which alone can provide the incentive for increased agricultural production. Moreover, the expansion of agriculture needs more equipment and industrial goods like fertilisers, for which larger investments are required in the industrial sector. We would therefore emphasize that the greater importance proposed to be attached to industry in the Second Plan is not in opposition to agriculture but is only a complement to the same designed not only to bring about a balanced growth of the economy but also to facilitate the expansion of agriculture and, even more important, to reduce the surplus population on land and raise the level of living of those left in agriculture. The economy needs both an agricultural base and an industrial base; these are not in conflict but are really complementary, and, beyond a certain initial stage of development, the growth of one conditions and facilitates the growth of the other. Hence the greater priority assigned to agriculture in the First Plan and that proposed to be assigned to industry in the Second Plan. All the same, we would underline the importance of maintaining and expanding agricultural production in the Second Plan period. There should be no feeling of complacency on the agricultural front because of the currently easy position in regard to foodgrains. Every effort must be made to step up the production of foodgrains and raw materials, and a suitable proportion of the investment contemplated in the Second Plan, especially in the field of heavy industry, must be linked with this objective; and there should also be built up during the period sufficient reserves of foodgrains and essential raw materials that will give stability to

the economy and prevent sudden falls in the pace of its general economic development.

18. We note that the tentative Plan-frame gives high priority to what are known as heavy industries and that consumer goods do not figure prominently in the investment pattern. The explanation for this lies predominantly in the fact that a high capital-output ratio is assumed in the case of both factory consumer goods and consumer goods emerging from the small scale and village industries sector. In the case of factory consumer goods, the full utilization of excess capacity is expected to lead to a considerable increase in the volume of output without any significant increase in the volume of fixed capital; in the case of non-factory consumer goods, labour is more important than capital equipment and the capital-ouput ratio is expected to be much more favourable than in the case of the organized industrial sector. It may be added that the investment in consumption goods industries, both factory and non-factory, though small in amount as compared with that in the so-called heavy industries, is nevertheless designed to bring about an increase in output of about 25% (20% in factory consumption goods and 33% in non-factory consumption goods) during the Plan period. A great deal of special effort will be required to achieve this objective, especially in the field of organization; and this is not going to be easy. We shall revert to this subject before the end of this section.

19. The important place assigned to power, transport, and communications is also a part of the same scheme for bringing about not only a balanced development of the economy but also to endow it with the capacity for self-propelling and accelerated growth. Economic overheads involve heavy investment; but they yield rich dividends in the form of making possible an all-round expansion of the economy; and there can be no denying the need for assigning an important place to these heads in the investment programme contemplated for the Second Plan.

20. The Plan also assigns a great deal of weight to construction the bulk of which is really of the nature of investment in fixed capital for economic and social overheads and which must be taken in conjunction with the contemplated increase in the annual expenditure on social and allied developmental services of about Rs. 100 crores in the Second Plan period as compared with the level expected to be reached in the last year of the First Plan period. Social overheads have a dual purpose; on the one hand, they represent

20

investment in human capital and promote an increase in productivity; on the other hand, they represent an end-product in themselves and bring about a direct addition to consumption services
and thereby promote a rise in the level of living; which is after
all the final objective of planning.   Hence it is that there is always
a special pressure exerted for stepping up the level of expenditure
on social overheads in terms of both investment outlay and current
expenditure.   There is also the further complication in the case
of our country that the basic levels of remuneration of many of
those engaged in the supply of social overhead services are below
reasonable standards and there is therefore strong pressure for using
available funds for raising these levels rather than using them for
expanding the supplies of these services.   There is no simple answer
to the questions raised by this problem.   All that we can say is that
a certain minimum level of expenditure on social overheads is an
essential condition for economic development; while further expansion of this expenditure is a concomitant of the growth of this development.   We may express the same thing in a different way by
saying that both investment and expenditure on social services
must become increasingly important with every successive Plan
period.   For the purposes of the Second Plan period, we are satisfied that the level assigned to this category in the investment programme is as far as we can go, taking into account the resources available and the need for building up our economic overheads, though
we cannot certainly express ourselves as satisfied with the position
in absolute terms.   That is really no more than saying that the economic development contemplated in the Second Plan period is no
more than a second stage in a long journey the end of which will
be reached only after many more Plan periods.   There is no point
in acting as if we have reached the goal before we have gone even
half-way towards it.

21.   It will be noticed that the pattern of investment outlay set
out in this section assigns an important place to stocks.   We have
already explained the importance of holding enough stocks of foodgrains and essential raw materials in order to facilitate the smooth
functioning of the development programme and provide some
insurance against the risks due to possible failures of the monsoon
or other interruptions in supplies.   We would only urge in this
context the importance of undertaking and completing as quickly
as possible the scheme for licensed warehouses recommended by the
Rural Credit Survey Committee.

22. In considering the structure of the Second Plan, it is even more important to consider its employment aspect. It needs no saying that our major problem is one of unemployment and under-employment. In the urban areas, besides the several lakhs of persons seeking employment through the employment exchanges, there are others who have not registered themselves; and in addition there is a considerable volume of under-employment and disguised unemployment prevalent among those who are shown as occupied in small industries, trade, and miscellaneous services. In the rural areas, the findings of the Agricultural Labour Enquiry reveal the presence of a considerable measure of both unemployment and under-employment among agricultural labourers; the same is also true of rural artisans and workers engaged in miscellaneous services. There is also the undoubted presence of under-employment and disguised unemployment revealed by the vast numbers of the so-called earning dependants who, by definition, do not earn enough even to sustain their own maintenance. Then there are the culti-vators of small and uneconomic holdings among whom there is a great deal of disguised unemployment. Among the estimates that have been placed before us, the lowest shows that leaving out the problem of disguised unemployment and under-employment among the cultivators, about 34 lakhs of people are wholly unemployed and there is a volume of under-employment equivalent to 49 lakhs of man-years, the major portion of the incidence of both being found in the rural areas. In addition to all this, there is the problem of employment created by the annual additions to the labour force estimated at about 1.8 million resulting from the normal growth of the population. The problem is indeed of enormous dimensions; and it would be too much to expect that it can all be solved within the Second Plan period. All the same, an attempt has to be made; and it has to be as big as our resources can permit. The tentative Plan-frame visualizes that about 10 to 12 million people will find employment during the Plan period, the investment pattern being specially designed to make this possible. It must be pointed out that the figure mentioned above does not refer to jobs as such in the sense of work on wages or salaries; a part will undoubtedly be jobs of this type; but a part will be in the form of employment opportunities that will enable so many more self-employing workers to obtain their livelihood. Even as it is, the number of self employing workers is much larger than that of hired workers; and the position is not likely to undergo a material change during the Second Plan period.

23. It is expected that a large number of workers will be employed in construction, which includes constructional activity of various kinds, including those required for both economic and social over-heads. There is also some likelihood of increase in the number of workers in mining and in the organized as well as the hand sector of industry. Employment opportunities, particularly for self-employed workers, are expected to grow in the sectors of trade and miscellaneous services largely as a result of the increase in economic activity resulting from the Plan, while paid employment for hired workers will increase largely in the sphere of public administration and social services. Incidentally, this is also expected to eliminate the growing unemployment among the educated classes in the country.

24. The pattern of employment opportunities visualized above rests to a large extent on the ability of the system to organize the labour force in the country, while the achievement of the targets set forth in regard to industrial consumption goods rests upon the ability to organise the sector of small industries and hand trades in the country. Both these involve large problems of organiza-tion and unless these are successfully tackled, it would be difficult to implement the Plan either in respect of its employment or its investment programme. Too much emphasis cannot therefore be laid on the task of reorganization, which is practically the king-pin of the success of the Plan; and much more attention needs to be paid to this aspect of planning than has been done so far.

25. The other important problem is one of organizing the supply of labour for whom jobs are to be found in the Second Plan period. Theoretically, the existence of a large volume of unemploy-ment and the substantial additions that are made to the labour force every year by the growth of population should perhaps make such organization unnecessary. In actual fact, however, labour in India has a great deal of lack of mobility as between rural and urban areas, and as between different States. It also suffers a great deal from lack of training either in skills or even in disciplined or regular hours of work. There is also the further fact, so glaringly revealed by the findings of the Agricultural LabourEnquiry and the National Sample Survey rounds, that large sections of the working force in rural areas obtain either wages or incomes much below the national average; and social justice demands that this class, which in a way is the most exploited class in the country, is given the first chance to improve its condition when new jobs are being

created in the country. Moreover, the incidence of distribution of this class is unevenly spread over different parts of the country and social justice demands that special attention is directed to what may be called the distressed areas in the country as distinguished from other areas which are better off, though in absolute terms their condition is no matter for satisfaction either. In view of these facts, a suggestion has been made for the organization of a National Labour Force, recruited from the classes which at present have either little or no income and particularly from those areas where the incidence of economic distress is comparatively high.

26. This proposal might be likened in its effect to that of the continuous recruitment in the army during war. The agricultural labourers, small farmers, etc., are not employed all round the year. The experience of war has shown that provided full time employment at reasonable rates is available, comparatively large number of adult males from such areas can be released full time and are fully mobile for employment. If it is possible to make use of such a labour corps in particular aspect of the general programme of development a number of advantages may arise. Firstly, it will withdraw significant number from labour in the countryside and thus relieve the unemployment and under-employment situation in many parts. Secondly, it will create a mobile force which can, as in the army, be fully trained in a variety of skills required for purposes of the development plan. This training may have an important civic aspect also. The labour force may form a revolving body from which suitable recruits can be obtained for new and growing scattered townships and centres of industrial and other activity. We suggest a careful examination of the proposal to organize a National Labour Force.

27. We would emphasize special attention being paid in planning of all works programmes to areas which are backward in any way, e.g., where communications are poor, climatic or other conditions unfavourable, the economy largely unmonetized, agriculture insecure, the standard of living low or which are inhabited by aborigines or other similar classes. These areas not only require the works programmes but also specially need the employment opportunities offered by them. We take it that when this attempt is made at deliberately opening or developing the backward tracts the economic, cultural or other adverse effects of the process will be guarded against in advance.

28.   It is also important to provide a positive policy for the stimulation of additional employment opportunities for self-employed
persons, particularly in view of the fact that the major portion of
the additional employment visualized in the Plan is in this field.
In this connection, we would recommend the development of a
large number of small towns widely distributed over different parts
of the country into industrial townships with planned provision
for small-scale and light industries.   Unlike the townships for
refugees that had been set up without due care for their employment potential, the towns proposed for development should be
selected after the most careful inquiry undertaken by competent
persons, in each region or locality and after most careful examination of the raw materials, markets, and other relevant factors
in the region.   There was a good analogy for this in the trading
estates that had been set up in England in the post-depression
period, and they could well be set up in the first instance in the
community project areas and National Extension Service blocks.
Thus, a new link could be established between the rural areas and
the urban areas, and what is called urbanization would not only
increase employment in the country but also add to its regional
spread, promote regional self-sufficiency, encourage a fruitful inter-
change between rural and semi-urban areas, and take economic
development into the regions which need it the most, viz., rural
India. It must be emphasized, however, that these industrial
townships in rural India will have to be planned from below and
cannot come from the top. Planning of small-scale industries,
consumption goods industries, and processing industries involves
the intelligent cooperation and participation of many thousands
of people and can only be undertaken at the district level; the
Centre can help with finance and technical aid, but the initiative
and the planning must come from the people of the districts and
regions concerned in the country.

29.   Finally, there is the question of the relation between small-
scale and large-scale industries in the field of consumption goods.
As we have already pointed out every attempt should be made to
bring about the fullest possible utilization of existing capacity
in the factory consumption goods industries; but we do not con-
template, for the Second Plan period at any rate, any significant
increase in their installed capacity.   This is not only because we
want to concentrate our scarce resources of foreign exchange and
essential materials on the setting up and expansion of the heavy

industries and economic overheads ; but also because we want to
provide more employment opportunities for those who are already
engaged in the small-scale and cottage industries and find employment for the new additions that are being made to the labour force
every year. Hence the emphasis on small-scale and cottage industries in the Second Plan.

30. The fact remains, however, that these hand industries
are technically inferior and cannot obviously face unaided the
competition of factory industries. At the same time, the needs
of development with its accent on increased productivity cannot
be reconciled with a continuance of the present inferior technical
level of the existing hand trades. It is therefore necessary to have
a Common Production Programme that will provide a secure
market for the products of these industries and at the same time
provide for gradual improvement of techniques and skills among
their workers. Details of such a programme will need careful
working out, but it can be stated at this stage that there will have
to be organized on a regional and a national scale cooperative and
other forms of organization for the supply of raw materials and
finance and for the marketing of finished products of the workers
engaged in hand industries. A beginning will also have to be
made in setting up a special sales organization for these industries.
At the same time, every attempt will have to be made to set up
increasingly efficient norms of work, and facilities and incentives
provided for reaching these norms. All these imply a tremendous
challenge to the organizational talent of the country ; and on the
degree of success with which this challenge is met will depend the
success of the whole scheme of a socialistic pattern of society, with
employment for all and decentralization and wide distribution
of both economic activity and economic advantages. We cannot
emphasize too strongly the important, almost the crucial, place
which this occupies in the Second Plan. A successful solution
of this problem together with the setting up of the economic and
social overheads including heavy industries envisaged in the Plan
will make possible much faster and larger development in the next
Plan period.

31. To sum up, the structure of the Plan that is visualized for
the Second Plan period provides for increased capital formation
and also for increased consumption. It emphasizes the importance of economic overheads and heavy industries in creating the
base for larger and faster economic development in subsequent

years. It underlines the need for looking after employment and
sets out a pattern of decentralized and small-scale economic activity
that will not only deal with the problem of unemployment and
of growing numbers but also with that of creating a socialistic
pattern of society that can function within a democratic set-up
and reconcile development and increased productivity with individual initiative and a large and fair field for all small units of economic activity. The structure that we have outlined cannot come
by itself. It needs organization for being brought into existence;
and in it lies a challenge to the organizational talent of our people.

III. POLICY AND INSTITUTIONAL IMPLICATIONS

32. In this part of the memorandum we consider the regulatory
and institutional set-up required to implement the Plan. We
assume as basic the social philosophy appropriate to Indian federal
democracy progressing towards a socialistic pattern of society.
In terms of economic organization and activity we interpret this
as denoting the following salient characteristic. In a society com-
posed chiefly of small decentralized units of economic activity
in which the increase in scale required in any activity is brought
about chiefly through mutual cooperation, horizontal and vertical,
and in which centralization and very large-scale operation are
resorted to only to the extent necessary to derive appropriate advantage from modern technology, the role of the State assumes
the following forms in the main : (i) Central planning, direction and conduct of economic activity to the extent necessary for
rapid economic development and increase of welfare ; (ii) State
assistance and participation in the formation and conduct of cooperative units ; and (iii) State action to eliminate or to counter the
effects of the continuance of privilege or the exercise of monopoly
power.

33. In considering the exercise of State authority we start with
the assumption of a continuance of the existing forms of regulation
and control of economic activity. In the context of this report,
the most important of these are capital issue control, the regulation
of establishment, location and operation of certain types of industrial units, control over the imports of capital goods and consumer
goods, control over the allocation of products like cement and steel,
control over the exports of selected commodities. The recommendation we would make in relation to existing regulations is that the
fullest coordinated use be made of them for a proper and detailed

implementation of the Plan. It is also assumed that legislation will shortly be enacted which will more adequately regulate the activities of public companies, and in particular to deal with the problem of managing agency and the concentration of economic power that it creates in the private sector.

34. We do not suggest any radical departure from the Industrial Policy Declaration of 1948. In fact, the sphere of State activity indicated in that resolution will be more fully covered as a result of investment in this Plan. It may also be found necessary, during the Plan period, to include within the public sector some activities closely related to the present declared scope, such as, basic minerals. The proper organization of coal production in the country and conservation and utilization of coal resources may also require including that industry in the public sector. Similarly, the special importance that will now be attached to production of small establishments will make it necessary to include not only the generation but also the distribution of electric power fully within the public sector. While we do not recommend any significant extension of the public sector beyond the terms of policy accepted by Government, we must make it clear that there is no objection in principle to such extension. In fact, the limiting factor is one of being able to cope with the administrative burden that would result from such extension. The cost of compensation may also have to be considered. If, however, during the course of the Plan period, circumstances become either more favourable from the administrative point of view or if it is found that opportunities for monopolistic or quasi-monopolistic exploitation are increasing in the private sector, there should be no objection to a further extension of the public sector. State trading in exports of jute, for example, was recommended many years ago by a representative committee consisting of administrators, businessmen, etc. In view of the peculiar position of these exports and the methods of trading in them, it is worth examining again whether State trading in jute should not be undertaken.

35. We are not in a position to make specific recommendations at this stage, but we would certainly emphasize the need for Government to examine each possibility of extension of the public sector in any important activity where, because of the policy under the Plan or other factors, a group of producers or traders are reaping special advantages.

36. While we do not suggest in the near future any general extension of the public sector, it would, certainly, be necessary for

21

implementing the Plan to extend the scope of the regulatory regime in particular directions. Thus confining to hand industries all increase in consumption goods during the Second Plan period will make it necessary to extend the operation of licensing legislation to include even processing activities. The best way of dealing with the situation would be for all State Governments to bring within licensing and regulatory legislation such establishments carrying out the processing and preparation of primary products and the production of consumer goods as are not covered by the existing Regulation of Industries Act.

37. A number of other regulations on consumption goods industries will follow from the common production plan for machine and hand industries in particular spheres. The division of market between machine and hand industry is sought to be maintained, today in the case of cloth production by a system of excises and subsidies on the one hand and reservation of fields on the other. The principle of reservation may not be so easily applicable to all industries and in their case a comparatively stable relation between prices of hand and machine products could be maintained only through excises and subsidies. There may be doubts whether these purely fiscal measures will prove successful and if these doubts were justified, other measures may be required to implement effectively a common production programme. In any case, the organization of increased production through hand industry will require considerable effort in distribution of supplies of technical and financial assistance to the dispersed producers and the collection and sale of their product. This would be largely done through cooperatives and as problems encountered will, in part, be similar to those dealt with by the Rural Credit Survey Committe in the case of agricultural production, the same expedients could be used in this case as well. In relation to technical guidance, and purchase and sale, the problems of cottage industry may, however, be different and more difficult. Bringing about increased production through this agency will, therefore, require as we have already mentioned, very considerable organizational effort in the Plan period. Any failure in this effort will create a difficult situation. On the one hand, there may be shortage of production by hand industry through inability of cooperatives to organize production or to carry out sales of products and their distribution. And on the other, there may be profiteering by producers and traders in that situation. If such a situation arises, it may be necessary for

the State to intervene and to consider the possibility of State trading of products. In the initial stages of the organization of this production it may, however, be wiser not to undertake State trading in this sphere.

38. As the spheres common to machine and hand industry will cover a large number of consumption goods in general use, the prices and supplies of goods over this large sphere will have to be constantly under State observation and regulation. In a number of important producers' goods, such as cement and steel, the existing allocation controls will continue, and price controls could be imposed, if necessary. This leaves mainly the prices of agricultural goods for consideration. In the present context, the stability of agricultural prices has special importance. Already Government have announced their intention and readiness to put a floor to prices of some agricultural products. Government's ability to do this effectively depends on their having an operative system which extends to all parts of the country. From this point of view, an early implementation of the recommendations of the Rural Credit Survey Committee regarding warehousing, processing and marketing of agricultural produce is of the utmost importance. It is only the setting up of the warehouses etc., recommended by the Committee that will put the State in a position to meet emergencies. We recommend that the warehousing system should be used by the State for purchase and sales of buffer stocks of agricultural commodities not only for the purpose of dealing with any sharp fall in agricultural prices such as we are witnessing today but also with the objective of preventing any sharp seasonal fall or rise in prices. Need for action in this regard may arise either in all commodities all over the country or only in an individual important commodity in particular regions. Such a system of buffer stocks will not only serve the limited purpose of evening out seasonal fluctuations but would come in useful and serve even larger purposes if the occasion arises. For example, the system could be put to use in case of an adverse monsoon or a sharp inflationary rise in prices.

39. The Government of India has taken an important policy decision recently by its announcement regarding creation of a State Bank of India through nationalization of the Imperial Bank and certain other States associated banks. We welcome this decision and strongly recommend its early implementation in full. It is of the utmost importance to bring into existence as early as possible a State Bank of India operating over the whole of the country

at the level envisaged by the Rural Credit Survey Committee. The regulation of activities in the sphere of banking and through banks may have considerable importance in the planning effort. For this purpose early implementation of the policy announced recently is an important and essential step forward.

40. The inevitably increased importance of the public sector in economic activity makes the problem of increasing its efficiency of vital importance to the success of planned development. Though it is not correct to say that the efficiency of the public sector today is necessarily below that of the private sector, it is clear that in itself, it is not too high and further that it could with considerable advantage be greatly increased. No definite pattern or organization of units in the public sector has yet been evolved in India. There is not enough experience in the matter, neither has any particular type shown definite success. We have no bias in favour of any particular type of organization and feel that considerable research and experimentation on the operation of different types of units in the public sector will be extremely worthwhile. The experimentation need not be confined to purely public organization but may well be extended to public-cum private organizations where the State holds full ultimate control and uses the private agency as a partner and as the agency of management. The general efficiency of administration is an equally important consideration which requires equal attention.

41. We may draw attention to a danger that is inherent in the type of mixed economy we have viz., unless adequate care is taken the slowest ship may set the pace of the convoy and inefficient units may get undue protection. The question of incentives and disincentives should be, therefore, very carefully studied and adequate and effective measures taken.

42. The State partnered cooperative seems now to be generally accepted as the most important type of organization in the future of economic development in India. Observation of its development, adaptation and success for various types of activities and in various contexts is, therefore, of great importance.

43. One of the gravest obstacles to undertaking a more ambitious programme of development in most directions today is the general state of unpreparedness of our society for the effort in most directions. The most important features of this are lack of trained personnel and of suitable organizations. The first lack is felt in all aspects of development of social welfare or related activities.

Teachers, doctors, technicians of all kinds are found to be in short supply the moment any large expansion is contemplated. But even more important is the organizational backwardness. This is experienced in every sphere. It is felt in the administrative structure, its efficiency and its capacity to carry out additional responsibilities; it is experienced in local governmental authorities; it is seen in the lack of established and effective pattern for conduct of economic activity in the public sector. These difficulties are patent today in attempted development along established lines. They are felt all the more keenly when orientation of the economy, on the now agreed lines of decentralized self-employment or co-operative activity is attempted. The manifold advantages of such an organization can be reaped only when the large work it involves by way of distribution of supplies and collection of product, of storage and finance, of technical guidance and administrative supervision is efficiently organized and carried out. The creation of such organization is an immense national task without whose accomplishment the proper development of agriculture and rural industry in particular will be well-nigh impossible. One of the reasons why in our opinion we cannot aim higher today is this lack in many directions. One of the most important tasks of the next five year plan must, therefore, be to remedy this grave handicap and defect. The energies of Government and of all constructive workers in the country must be turned in this direction so that at the end of the plan period the economy and the society will be in a position to take a much greater step forward and to achieve a rate of development which would not only be bold but spectacular.

44. We now turn to consideration of policies which are not only important for the execution of the Plan but are also important as indicating the determination of the State to progress towards the socialistic pattern. The first set of policy decisions to be considered in this regard are those relating to land reform. The content of this programme has by now been fairly clearly determined. It consists mainly of four measures; consolidation of holdings which has an important bearing on productive efficiency in agriculture, operation of the ceiling which makes available land for redistribution to landless labourers without unduly lowering the size of any unit, the floor to holdings which makes it impossible for units smaller than of certain size to be cultivated as independent farming units, and cooperative farming which would bring in all such uneconomic units into farms large enough to be operated efficiently. The

content of the land reform programmes has already been announced and has raised wide expectations throughout the country. The announcement has also had some adverse effects on the situation through the action of landholders, through evictions and the like, to safeguard their interests in anticipation of the policy. It appears to us of the most urgent importance for the State Governments all over the country to recognise certain basic principles of action in regard to all the four constituents of this programme, to formulate definite policies of action at as early a stage as possible and to implement them. The best course as well as the most logical, of course, is to bring the whole programme into operation simultaneously. The operation of the floor raises, however, certain difficulties; apart from the practicability of forming quickly an enormous number of cooperative farming societies. These difficulties are related to the extent of employment that is available in the economy. Similar difficulties however do not attach to that part of the programme that relates to the imposition of a ceiling on holdings and the consolidation of scattered holdings. We recommended therefore that immediate steps be taken to impose a ceiling on agricultural holdings and redistribute the land thus released to landless labourers. We also suggest that action be taken in regard to consolidation of holdings without delay. As early as possible when enough experience has been gained in the countryside regarding operation of other cooperative effort and when adequate employment has been generated, the other two features of the land reform programme should be put into operation.

45. The operation of the ceiling and redistribution of land to the landless will bring about considerable lessening of inequality in rural society. The acceptance of the idea of a ceiling on land must lead, in our opinion, logically to the acceptance of the parallel concept of a ceiling on all personal incomes for the urban and industrial sectors. This has been already mentioned by the Taxation Enquiry Commission and we feel it vital that a policy announcement regarding this be made in the Second Five Year Plan of Government. Two other recommendations of the Taxation Enquiry Commission we would endorse for immediate action towards lessening inequalities. These are : (a) a steepening of the estate duties and (b) imposition of the Capital Gains tax. We expect an appreciation of the values of all kinds of property because of the operation of a plan of development and feel it necessary that the above steps be taken at the beginning of the period of a bold plan. It may,

further, be useful to conduct enquiries into increase of land values in urban areas and the spread in values of salaries. In case of the latter, we would recommend the inquiry not to be confined to salaries of officials but to embrace within it salaries (and total spending power) of individuals in private business also.

46. Lessening of inequality is a two-fold process. One of its aspects is the lowering of unduly large incomes. An equally important or, perhaps in the long run the more important, aspect is that of increasing or making more secure the incomes of the poorest. In this connection we would welcome greater progress, wherever possible, in the standardization of wages and fuller implementation of the Minimum Wages legislation in the country, due regard being paid to the effect of wage increases on employment. Both should reduce the total range of differentials in wage payment. It is not possible at this stage to recommend any general social security schemes which would have wide application, or would materially lessen insecurity of incomes. We would, however, recommend exploration of the possibilities of the State offering life insurance schemes wide-spread throughout the country. In the absence of measures of social security as such, we must to look to the fullest extension of social service expenditure for doing something in this behalf. However, if this expenditure is really to result in lessening inequalities and in materially improving the conditions of the most disadvantaged, special care must be taken by the State authorities to see that it is deliberately routed and administered in such a manner that its benefits, in the largest measure, go to the poorest, the most disadvantaged and the most insecure classes.

47. We have dealt so far with some of the policy implications of the size and the structure of the Plan, as prescribed in the "Frame" for the Second Plan period. What we would emphasize in conclusion is that unless these policy implications are duly considered, and rapid and effective action taken thereon, the chances of successfully implementing either the size or the structure of the proposed Plan will be seriously jeopardized. Even if the different parts of the Plan are fairly well balanced and the size of the effort involved is not beyond the country's capacity, it would be wrong to entertain optimistic expectations merely on the technical soundness of the targets proposed. Besides these targets, there are, initially major assumptions regarding the capacity of the country and especially of Government to put through the programme as proposed.

For these assumptions to materialize a big organizational effort will be called for. Planning does not mean merely a programme of large investment, especially not when the objective is not merely an increase in output but also the creation of a socialistic pattern of society. It is only when there is a firm legislative and administrative base that it is possible to think in terms of doubling the rate of progress in the Second Plan period, of increasing capital formation, of raising levels of living, and providing the machinery for accelerated development in the future. We cannot therefore emphasize too strongly the importance of facing up boldly and without hesitation the legislative and administrative implications of a bigger and a bolder plan. The Second Five Year Plan is a challenge to the nation. It requires effort and substantial efforts at that and on a large and organized scale. It requires austerity and restraint on the part not only of those whose incomes are high but even of those whose incomes are not so high. What is required is a national effort and a national effort can be forthcoming only if it is clearly visible to the people that there will emerge from it a new and desired type of society. Hence it is that we lay so much emphasis on the policy implications of the Plan-frame that has been placed before us.